MW0038734Ø

KEEPING *the* OLDER HORSE YOUNG

A Natural Approach to Revitalizing Horses 10 and Over

ELEANOR M. KELLON, V.M.D.

Breakthrough

Dedicated with love and gratitude to my parents,

James and Eleanor Waldron,

and my children

—Erica, Andrea, Craig and John—

the first for their guidance and support

through the trials and challenges of my younger years

and the second for teaching me first-hand what that was all about!

Text copyright (c) 2000 by Eleanor Kellon VMD
Design & graphics copyright (c) 2000 by Breakthrough Publications Inc
Photography copyright as noted below

All rights reserved. No part of this work covered by copyright herein may be reproduced or used in any form or by any means—graphic, electronic, or mechanical, including photo-copying, recording, taping, or information storage and retrieval systems—without permission in writing from the publisher.

For information address:
Breakthrough Publications Inc
www.booksonhorses.com

The following products mentioned in this book are Registered in the U.S. Patent and Tradesmark Office: Actimune (ActiVet Bio, Ltd) Adequan™, (Luitpold Pharmiceuticals, Anthelcide EQ, (Norden), Banamine™. (Schering), Benzelmin, (Syntex), Betadine, (Purdue Frederick), body Builder™, (Equi-Aid), CortaFlx, (Equine America), Ester-C, (Inter-Cal Corp), Equipoise™, (Squibb), Equizole, (MSD AgVet), G.U.T. (Uckele Health), GlutaSyn (Vita-Flex), Immune One arabinogalactan powder or Immune One Pellets - Source One Naturals, (Zimectrin, Eqvalan, Rotectin and Equimectrin), (Farnam), Missing Link™ (Designing Health), Nutrient Buffer (Vita Royal), Panacur, (American Hoechst). Strongid C, (Pfizer), Strongid P, Strongid T (Pfizer),Thyrol L, (Lloyd, Inc) Triple Crown Senior Horse Feed, (Equine Specialty Feeds), Winstrol™, (Winthrop) YeaSacc (Diamond V Mills).

ISBN 0-914327-89-5
Book design and layout by Breakthrough Publications Inc
Manufactured in the United Sates of America

Photographs copyright of the following photographers: Tricia Booker (pages 2,8), Amy Dragoo (pages 55,63,64,85), Lee Foley (pages 41, 83, 204, 279), Maureen Gallatin (pages 13, 16, 26, 29, 35, 43, 79, 92, 93, 94, 98, 99, 103, 120, 121, 122, 131, 160, 163, 174, 191, 192, 207, 209, 219, 220, 222, 227, 235, 244, 247, 251, 274, 284), Gemma Giannini (217, 270), Shawn Hamilton, CliX Photography (pages 37, 211, 213, 214), Charles Hilton (page 14), Shirley Ruth Johnson (pages 31, 97, 205, 302), Isabel Kurek (pages 133, 143, 152), Marie Smith (page 269), Susanna and Jim Thomas (pages 104, 130), Katherine Wolcott (page 111), Mark Walpin (page 7), Dorothy Woodward, CliX Photography (pages 18, 22)
Illustrations: Kip Carter (pages 5, 159 and 165)

CONTENTS

INTRODUCTION

All around us there are signs that the focus of medical care is changing. We are moving from the days when major battles were being fought against life-threatening infections to a time when a longer expected life span results in the challenges being focused on degenerative diseases—age-related problems. Considerable research dollars are being directed both into the study of specific age-related diseases, like arthritis, and into the very process of aging.

A parallel change is occurring in how the medical profession sees its major role. The emphasis is shifting from the treatment of diseases to preventing them. Insurance companies offer reduced premiums to policy holders who do not smoke and are increasingly willing to pay for routine/preventative health care visits. The reason for this is simple. Statistics show it is less expensive in the long run to invest in keeping people healthy and catching problems early than to treat advanced serious illnesses.

A natural outgrowth of the focus on preventing disease is growing interest in creating optimal health. It is not enough anymore just to get by and be free of a major life-threatening disease. People are not satisfied just to live longer—they want to be active and feel good, too. As a result, less emphasis is being placed on drugs to make you feel well and more on what is needed to build a healthy body and keep it that way—vitamins, minerals, basic diet, exercise and the environment.

The majority of research into aging and maintaining wellness has been done in laboratory animals with the focus on applying the knowledge to people. However, aware animal owners are also pressuring their veterinarians to help their charges live longer, happier and more active lives. The keep 'em healthy approach to medical care is rapidly spilling over into how we manage our animals, often with very rewarding results. In fact, horses often respond quicker and more dramatically to such things as nutritional supplements—not too surprising since most equine diets are borderline if not deficient in one or more key nutrients and the focus in equine nutrition has always been on supplying the bare minimum necessary to prevent full-blown deficiency states (light-years away from what optimal intake would be).

In this book, we will take at look at what aging is and what causes it, then apply this knowledge to a plan for forestalling those aspects of aging that are within our power to influence and look at positive, healthful ways to combat many of the age-related ailments that plague older horses. Aging may be inevitable, but there is plenty of room for improving both the length and quality of our horses' lives.

CHAPTER ONE

WHAT IS AGING?

Seems like a straightforward enough question. Aging is when you get older, wear out and die.

But what really happens during aging? Does the body just wear out like a carpet in a high traffic area or burn out like a bonfire? Yes and no.

There are some aspects of aging that are largely preset and unavoidable. Every species has a maximum life-span. For people, it is somewhere around 120 years. We don't really know what it is for horses, but a reasonable estimate would appear to be about 1/3 of that, although the oldest recorded age of a horse is alleged to be 62. Obviously, very few members of either species even come close. Overall health fails and a variety of diseases/disorders intervene. Aging and its inevitable consequence, death, is therefore a combination

Not all horses seem to age at the same rate. Monopoly, owned by Beth Underhill, won the $100,000 HITS Grand Ocala at age 20.

of preset inherent limitations on life-span that we cannot change (yet anyway) and outside influences. Researchers use the term premature aging to describe the various things that can cause an individual to become old and die before their time.

EARLY ADVANCES IN INCREASING LIFE-SPAN

Control of infectious diseases is the major factor responsible for a longer human life-span in the U.S., which increased from 47 years at the turn of the century to 76 years today. Animals instinctively know to avoid their own body wastes as well as other sick or dead animals. Even such ancient civilizations as the Egyptians had a rudimentary sewage disposal system in place. However, it wasn't until we learned about the marvels of the invisible world of micro-organisms and the advent of effective antiseptics that significant inroads started to be made in the control of infectious disease.

Real headway was not made until the discovery of penicillin and its stabilization into a useful drug in the 1930s and 1940s. A host of penicillin derivatives were discovered, then other classes of natural antibiotics and finally a wide assortment of synthetic antibiotics. Antibiotics have largely eliminated bacterial infection as a cause of premature death or permanent damage to organs in horses.

The use of vaccines is now considered a routine part of health care for horses, but they, too, are a relatively recent development. As recently as the 1950s, polio was a greatly feared disease with epidemics still occurring. It was not until the 1960s that the initial work of Jonas Salk, followed by modifications to the first crude vaccines by Albert Sabin, gave us the techniques needed to control and virtually eradicate polio and soon thereafter a whole host of viral infectious diseases that could kill or maim. Vaccines for horses rapidly followed.

Modern surgical techniques, shock/trauma treatment, cardiac bypass surgery, organ transplants and advances in fighting cancer are also helping doctors to deal with life-threatening situations and many of these new techniques are used with great success on horses. However, it is becoming more and more obvious that the challenge of the 21st century is going to be the fight against aging.

The Biological Clock and Other Unavoidable Causes

There are several theories floating around concerning the cause of aging, none completely satisfactory. Most explanations concerning unavoidable causes center on DNA—the genetic material of all cells that contains the information and instructions for cell functions.

Cells have limited ability to repair themselves. The major way in which our organs, bones and other parts heal is by replacing dead cells with new, healthy ones. One theory is that all cells have pre-programmed into them a finite number of times that they can divide. When that limit is reached, the last generation of cells begins to be damaged by internal and external insults until it is no longer functional. When enough cells in an organ cease to function, degenerative diseases begin to set in, like kidney failure or liver failure.

Another theory has to do with the way that DNA copies itself. You may recall from basic biology that when cells divide the two strands of DNA (which look like a ladder coiled in the shape of a spiral staircase) open up along the middle of their rungs. These two

DNA, the genetic material all cells are made of has been described as looking like a spiral staircase. How DNA divides when it copies itself may affect the rate at which a living thing ages.

strands are then copied by molecules of RNA. The end result is four strands of DNA instead of two. These single strands will recombine to form two paired DNA molecules, which then separate and form the core/nucleus of two new cells.

Scientists have learned that RNA does not copy the full length of the DNA strand and that at the ends of the DNAs are several protein units called telomeres. The telomeres are not essential to the normal functioning of the cells. They are believed to be a built-in protection to guarantee the RNA fully copies the important parts of the DNA. If RNA misses copying a little bit of the end of the DNA, nothing will be lost. However, scientists also now know that every time a cell divides it loses a little bit of the telomere. The theory is that once the telomere becomes shortened beyond a critical point, the DNA left at the ends uncopied will begin to contain important information that is not passed on to the next generation of cells. This causes imperfect cells that do not function normally, or stops division altogether, and aging begins.

PREVENTABLE CAUSES OF AGING– "PREMATURE AGING"

To understand how aging can be slowed and good health preserved well into old age, think of the body as analogous to a car engine. At birth, the parts are all perfectly clean and smooth and work together effortlessly. The engine is tuned to produce the peak power possible without waste of fuel. The electrical system fires every time, without shorts or other interruptions in conduction.

If you maintain the engine perfectly by changing filters before they become overloaded, always providing the correct fuel, change the oil religiously, etc., it will last far longer than if maintenance is overlooked. An extra 10,000, 20,000 maybe even 50,000 miles is possible if the engine is maintained and never abused. We know better than to simply take a car and run it without ever doing these things, thinking, "Oh well, it's going to break down/die sometime anyway," yet that is exactly the attitude too often taken toward preserving health.

Bright Zip, owned by John Lyons, performed at Equitana at age 24.

R.O. Sultan won the Best Condition 1996 World Endurance
Championship at age 19. The horse still competes at age 22.

Many things combine over time to damage/age an engine. Impurities in gasoline and the air form harmful wastes when gas is burned, physical wear and tear on parts causes grooving and tiny breaks in the metal, oil breaks down, filters clog, deposits form on spark plugs and battery terminals and the list goes on. Aging of the engine is the end result of all of these harmful things combining over time. The same thing is happening in the horse's body (and yours, too). If your engine seizes up on you after 40,000 miles because you ran it hard and never did any maintenance, used cheap gas, barely remembered to keep enough oil, water and transmission fluid in it, no one would be surprised. However, it is fair to say that the engine died prematurely since it had the potential to last two to three times as long. Again, exactly the same thing can happen to your horse.

I used the analogy of a car engine because most people are much more familiar with how their car engine works, and the types of things that can damage it, than with the functioning of the body.

In fact, mechanics really know more about maintaining engines, and the factors that cause wear and breakdown, than doctors and veterinarians do about preventing aging. We're learning, though.

CHAPTER TWO

PINPOINTING THE PREVENTABLE CAUSES OF AGING

You can keep your horse from aging before his time, possibly even halt or partially reverse aging changes you are already seeing, by knowing how to keep his body tuned up and serviced.

There is nothing magical about the formula for doing this—clean air, fresh water, proper diet and exercise. The trick is in knowing how to put together a general health package for the older horse that keeps him looking and feeling young for the longest time possible. To do that, we need to understand what factors have been identified as being important in aging.

WEIGHT

The latest aging research is finding there was some truth after all to the motto "You can't be too thin." The only reliable way to increase life-span in mammals is calorie restriction. Experiments have proven time after time, with various species, that controlling calorie intake can produce dramatic increases in life-span. Several biochemical differences have been identified between the lean and more rotund study animals, some of which will be mentioned below in specific categories. The bottom line appears to be that calorie restriction puts the entire metabolism in a survival mode. Sensitivity to important hormones, like insulin, is increased and more characteristic of much younger animals. Systems that protect against cellular damage show greatly increased activity in the calorie-restricted animals. Their bodies become super-efficient at absorbing and utilizing key nutrients and special attention is paid to the key organ systems when the time comes to divide up the available fuel, protein, vitamins and minerals.

There is no reason to believe findings would be any different if these studies were done with horses. This does not mean it is a good idea to drastically cut your horse's calorie intake. Such a measure could prove fatal to ponies. The study animals were all raised on calorie-restricted diets from birth. However, we also know from research and clinical experience that overweight older animals (or people) put on a sensible weight reduction diet and exercise program show improvement in many of the same areas where calorie-restricted experimental animals excel.

This 22-year-old Arabian mare, owned by Lynn Black, is in great shape for her age.

Avoiding excess weight in the older horse will keep his metabolism operating efficiently and also will avoid overstressing his back, tendons, ligaments and joints. The horse should not appear gaunt, but his ribs should be easily felt when you run your hand along the chest. We don't want his hip bones and withers sticking out, but they shouldn't be buried under layers of fat either. Appropriate diets for the older horse will be discussed in detail in the chapter on basic diet.

EXERCISE

Many horses are retired because of skeletal problems/lamenesses that limit their ability to exercise.

However, once regular exercise is stopped, the horse will quickly lose even more exercise capacity. Part of the reason for this is a loss in muscle mass and therefore in strength. Age is naturally associated with loss of muscle (which is replaced by fat), but the age-related shrinkage of muscle can largely be prevented by regular, formal exercise. Another age-related change is a decrease in the amount of elastic in connective tissues such as tendons. Elastin, as the name suggests, is the special component that allows these tissues to stretch. Again, regular exercise can do wonders to preserve the elasticity and

Regular exercise can do wonders to preserve the elasticity and flexibility of connective tissues. That's proven true for this trail-riding palomino.

flexibility of connective tissues, as can appropriate dietary supplements.

Joint problems are among the most common reasons for retiring a horse. While it is true that excessive pounding is only going to make the situation worse, stopping regular exercise is not the answer. Regular exercise not only improves the health of joint cartilage, it improves the outcome of specific joint supportive drugs and nutritional supplement programs. Turn out and giving your horse phenylbutazone (bute) are a prescription for joint destruction. There are far more effective ways to control pain, heal joints and preserve mobility. Every effective arthritis program includes regular exercise.

METABOLISM

Ever wonder why the eight-year-old racehorse can look older than your neighbor's 30-year-old pony or mixed-breed horse? Hot-blooded horses have higher metabolic rates than their more laid back counterparts. They are living life at a faster pace and tend to burn up or wear out faster as well. Many calories are wasted in maintaining their excessively high nervous energy. They rarely have a problem with being overweight, but their metabolism burns fuels very rapidly and often inefficiently. When foods are burned, potentially harmful by-products such as free radicals are produced. Studies on weight and aging revealed that weight-controlled animals had slower metabolic rates that resulted in more efficient burning of calories.

There is a fine line, however, between a metabolism that is

Getting enough vitamins through a healthy diet and/or supplements can help prevent free radical damage. Carrots are rich in vitamin A.

slowed and more efficient and one that is slowed too much by overly aggressive dieting. If you cut the horse's calories too much, his glandular and energy systems will not function effectively. He will be sluggish and not feel well.

It will actually be more difficult for the horse to achieve weight loss and an efficient metabolism under these circumstances. The same thing happens to people who crash diet.

Both over- and underactivity of the glandular systems in the horse can lead to premature aging. The finely tuned endocrine/glandular system is really what is ultimately responsible for the effective level of metabolism we are looking for. This includes not only the thyroid gland—which most people think of as controlling metabolism—but also the sex hormones, the adrenal glands (epinephrine, cortisone, electrolyte regulating hormones), the thymus gland (regulating immune responses) and the pancreas (insulin). A certain number of horses may need medications to correct endocrine abnormalities as they age. In most cases dietary adjustments, provision of key vitamins and minerals and sometimes nonprescription glandular supplements are a much better way to go.

FREE RADICAL DAMAGE

Somewhere along the line you have probably heard the term free radicals, probably in connection with vitamins. The free radical theory of aging (and disease) is the most widely accepted in the preventable causes category. It is also the most exciting theory, since it makes so much sense and you can actually do something about it.

Free radicals are molecules that have lost one of the electrons in their outer shell, either as the result of a chemical reaction or after being hit by another free radical. These molecules are very unstable and actively seek to get back that missing electron any way they can—stealing one from the nearest stable molecule they can find.

Free radicals are produced in the body all the time—from the

17

basic chemical reactions within a cell (e.g., generating energy from foods), from reactions between metals and oxygen, from the body's interaction with drugs and chemicals—anywhere that oxygen and metals/minerals are found in close proximity. Even an overload of reactive minerals that are essential in small amounts can produce widespread free radical damage.

This photograph of Banner, age 38, on an OTRA trail ride, shows that the process of aging is relative. Banner lived to age 40.

The best example of this is iron. Thousands of people are literally poisoning their horses every day when they give them high iron supplements. The immune system cells, especially the B cells that attack and destroy invading organisms, use reactions that create free radicals to destroy bacteria. An example of a free radical reaction involving oxygen outside the body is the formation of rust or the way an apple turns brown on its cut surface. In a sense, free radical production is the horse's body's equivalent of toxic waste—an inevitable by-product of otherwise beneficial processes.

Free radical damage to the body has been implicated in a wide variety of diseases that commonly show up with advancing age, including heart disease, cancers, weakened arteries and veins, diabetes, arthritis and weakening of the skin and tendons/ligaments. Wrinkles and sagging skin are in large part caused by the cumulative effects of free radical damage over the years.

The body has its own very elaborate system of mopping up free radicals and neutralizing them. There are antioxidant enzymes, which contain the trace minerals selenium, zinc or copper (sometimes iron) such as superoxide dismutase, antioxidant vitamins (A, C, E), and other naturally occurring substances the body produces to control free radicals such as lipoic acid or CoQ10. In addition, scientists have located other antioxidant substances that occur naturally in the diet and undoubtedly are very important in the antioxidant arsenal. These include the bioflavonoids, a group of chemicals that work with vitamin C and in their own right—including rutin, hesperidin and quercetin, and the family of chemicals called pynconogels, naturally found in high concentration in barks, leaves and seeds. Familiar pyn-conogel supplements for human (and equine) use include grape seed and pine bark. Even the types of fat you feed your horse will influence how well he can manage free radicals and inflammation in general. Supplying a diet adequate in classes of antioxidant nutrients needed to keep these functions working at an optimal level is one of the best defenses against aging and age-related diseases. New and potent antioxidants are being discovered all the time in whole, unprocessed foods.

MINERAL AND CHEMICAL TOXICITIES

Most people know that children who chew on lead-based paint chips become poisoned, that old copper piping in houses may make you sick and that industrial workers in a huge variety of industries can become sick (toxic) from chemical exposure. The horrible consequences of soldiers being exposed to chemical warfare agents such as Dioxin in contaminated Agent Orange are now evident. This type of illness may seem very remote from the way our horses live, and 30 years ago that might have been true. It's not true today.

For the last 15 to 20 years I have been coming across horses that have a constellation of problems that defy a complete explanation. They are not sick enough in most cases to have it interfere with performance but clearly are not in top form. Table 5-1 on page 87 lists the common problems often seen in combination in these horses.

In time, I began to consider such horses as being toxic. In almost every case, these horses were iron overloaded. When treated with high doses of antioxidant nutrients—vitamin E/selenium, vitamin C, grape seed extract, bioflavonoids, trace minerals—their tying-up, gastric ulcer symptoms and allergy-related problems would disappear, skin and hooves would improve dramatically. Other problems were not so easily fixed—especially those that seemed to have an endocrine (glandular) basis such as erratic blood glucose, fluctuating energy levels, poor stress tolerance and hypothyroidism. I went a step further and began to do hair mineral analysis, looking for toxic metals. Sure enough, every horse tested had high levels of at least one toxic mineral (often more), the most common being aluminum. This still did not get me very far in understanding the basis of the glandular problems—beyond just writing them off as caused by stress.

It was only after I learned of the work of Linsey McLean, a biochemist, and began delving into the available literature on environmentally linked diseases that a connection became clear. The relatively recent explosion in the manufacture of plastics, synthetic fabrics, pesticides, herbicides and other chemicals occurred long before industry or science had any idea about the toxicity of some of the waste they were producing. In fact the pilot scientific study that uncovered the almost incomprehensible toxicity of the chemical class Dioxins (safe lifetime intake of the most potent toxin in the group, TCDD, is less than 1/9,900,000 of a grain of salt!) was actually largely funded by the industry that produces it! Every human and animal on the planet now has these chemicals in their body—every one. Traces of the parent

A healthful diet is essential in any plan to keep a horse looking and feeling his best. Here we see the Morgan stallion, Serenity Intrigue, at age 30.

compounds, PCBs, were actually picked up at the South Pole for the first time in 1998—after strict regulatory controls regarding their release had been in effect. This is not some wild, radical doomsday prediction— it's a fact. Individuals vary widely in how susceptible they are to the effects of tiny amounts of chemicals in the environment, and what symptoms they will develop. There are plenty of other chemicals the horse is exposed to over his lifetime, including pesticides, nitrates, chemicals in fly sprays, wipes, etc. We consider them safe because he doesn't get sick right after you use them. However, these chemicals accumulate in body fat and internal organs. The levels rise over time, as the horse ages. Like free radicals, the results of millions of tiny accumulations over time eventually begin to show up in a variety of organs.

CHAPTER THREE

THE BASIC DIET

Introduction

If the horse does not eat enough, he becomes sluggish, weak, loses weight and eventually starves. Not exactly an earth-shattering observation. However, the easiest part of feeding a horse is providing him enough calories to keep his weight up. Diet does much, much more than just keep the horse going. It is the most important factor in his general health and performance. It can be the most important medicine you have, or can influence health in a negative way. A healthful diet is the core of any plan to keep a horse feeling his best and living the longest. Without it, you are wasting your time. You can feed your horse pounds of vitamins and other supplements every day but will never get the effects you are after if the basic diet

Diet does more than just keep the horse going. It's an important factor in health and performance.

is not correct.

To use diet effectively, we have to change the way we look at nutrition—just like we are changing how we look at health care. All nutritionists are trained to balance diets by looking at energy (calories) first. The amount of protein, fat, minerals and vitamins (if vitamins are even considered) is examined next. The goals a nutritionist has for creating a balanced ration usually result in compromises being made in the aspects of the diet that are most important to health. As soon as the nutritionist has come up with a combination of grains and hays that gives him/her the number of calories they are after, they begin making compromises with everything else.

Traditional ration balancing for animals first seeks to maintain weight and size. Then it tends to consider what it can get away with on the protein, vitamin and mineral front rather than what will result in optimal health.

The result is a long list of minimal requirements, but that very term, minimal, should be your first clue as to what kind of health you can expect if you follow them.

If you are following a household budget, you may sit down and figure out how much heating oil you will need to get through the winter. To save money, you request only that specific amount be delivered. If a cold snap hits and your burner must run harder, you could easily run out of oil. By allowing for only that minimum, you are flirting with disaster. When this happens with heating your house, the worst consequence is a very cold night, maybe a few frozen pipes and extra costs for burner start up and unscheduled delivery of oil that completely wipe out the savings you had counted on by limiting the amount of oil delivered in the first place. When it happens inside your horse's body, the consequences can be more serious.

The horse's body is a collection of hundreds of furnaces, each one requiring a different mix of vitamins and minerals to function properly. By providing only the projected minimums of these fuels, we risk shutdown on a daily basis. When a horse exercises without sufficient antioxidant defenses in his muscles, joints and tendons to protect them from all the damaging free radicals he is going to generate, or enough amino acids (proteins), vitamins and minerals to repair any physical damage, he will end up stiff and sore afterward and will have taken another little step down the road to aging. A horse using all his reserve of nutrients to combat the stress of cold weather may not have what he needs to mount an immune response to protect him from a virus.

Good nutrition can go a long way toward repairing all those little, isolated episodes of joint damage that would otherwise eventually add up to arthritis or preventing those respiratory infections that weaken his lungs and contribute to the development of allergies. Your horse will age soon enough from genetic causes. Why hurry the process along by settling for a diet that puts him constantly on the brink of day-to-day behind-the-scenes system failures that hurry the process along?

Special Needs of the Older Horse

Researchers have identified several dietary needs that are different for older horses and related to the common decline in how well their digestive tract breaks down and absorbs nutrients. These include:

- less efficient breakdown of fiber

- less efficient absorption of phosphorus

- probable need for higher vitamin C in diet (blood levels of vitamin C lower in older horses)

- need for higher quality protein sources but not excessive quantity of protein

There are commercial diets available formulated especially for seniors that address these special needs and, in some cases, may also offer a lower calorie density (presuming the horse does less work than younger animals) and may be easier to chew or digest. It is wonderful that specific attention is being focused on developing

Researchers have identified several dietary needs that are different for older horses. Some commercial feeds are now formulated specially for seniors.

products suitable for older horses.

However, there is a tendency, especially in feed companies and by some nutritionists, to focus on the few things we do know about different needs for older horses (e.g., less efficient phosphorus absorption) and proceed as if that is all there is to it. While it is sound, strict, scientific procedure to stick to the facts and only use information that has been rigidly proven, it is silly to assume that the information we now have is all that we need to know about dietary requirements of older horses. It makes more sense to assume that older horses probably have many special requirements (the few details already known proving that special requirements exist) than to assume they do not have special requirements until proven otherwise.

This may seem more like a philosophical argument than anything else, but it has very practical applications. For example, it makes little sense to focus only on phosphorus when in all likelihood the problems with phosphorus absorption apply to the other major minerals as well (calcium and magnesium). Trace mineral absorption (selenium, iodine, zinc, manganese, copper) is very variable even in younger, healthy horses. There is not much chance that it improves with age when digestive function is declining in general. Making phosphorus absorption more efficient is not going to have much effect unless you fit it into the big picture and work on getting all minerals in the diet at needed levels and in a form the older horse can most easily absorb.

The horse could be extinct if we wait for research done specifically in horses to confirm that sure enough the older horse has an increased need for calcium (or magnesium or zinc). It makes more sense to design a diet that hopefully will optimize both levels and absorption of all important minerals and vitamins.

On the practical end, the following will give you step-by-step instructions for looking at the older horse's diet and determining how to improve it so the horse gets all the needed nutrients.

TEETH

A major cause of weight loss and poor digestion of feeds in older horses is bad teeth. All horses should have their teeth carefully checked and filed (floated) every six months. In the case of older horses this is an absolute must. Many older horses chew poorly simply because their teeth have become long and misaligned by not having regular dental care.

It is especially important to find an equine dentist and/or veterinarian who does a thorough job. The last molars in the horse's mouth are very difficult to reach and file carefully, with the result they are often done less than perfectly. If this continues, they can grow large spikes (like tusks) of tooth that eventually cause pain when the horse eats. These may actually need to be ground down with a dremel tool rather than a file. This procedure absolutely requires the use of a mouth speculum.

The horse's front teeth (incisors) can also become so long they result in the mouth being out of alignment. Modern dentists will grind these down, too.

→

A mouth speculum looks like a torture device. It is a metal cage that slides into the horse's mouth and is cranked open to keep him from closing his jaws. This gives the dentist unrestricted access to the back teeth. However, used improperly it is extremely uncomfortable for the horse.

It is also a dangerous thing to have sitting in the horse's mouth when you are working up close. If the horse jumps or swings his head suddenly, e.g., because of pain, it can cause serious injury to the people working with the horse. If the dentist/veterinarian working on the horse is good at floating teeth, he/she will not need a speculum to get cooperation from the horse and will only use one if both hands are needed to work on the teeth (e.g., those large back spikes). Otherwise, the mouth is kept open by holding the tongue off to one side and out of the mouth while filing the teeth on the opposite side with the other hand. If a speculum must be used, the dentist/veterinarian may suggest the horse be given tranquilization or even a short-acting general anesthetic to allow the job to be done as quickly and smoothly (and safely) as possible.

Older horses are also more likely to develop problems with gum disease, broken or loose teeth and infected teeth. The best indicator of a serious problem along these lines is the development of a bad odor to the horse's breath. Appetite will drop off and chewing will be greatly slowed. The horse may also be reluctant to drink enough because the water causes pain. In fact, it is not that unusual for a horse with a serious dental problem to be brought to the veterinarian's attention because of problems with weakness, weight loss, constipation or even colic. Regular, meticulous dental examinations will catch these problems early. If you even suspect a mouth problem between check-ups, be sure to call the veterinarian or your equine dentist.

FIBER

Poor digestion of fiber is both a cause and a result of some of the digestive problems of older horses. Horses are designed to process large amounts of plant material—what we normally call roughage.

This includes hays and grasses. (Other things often considered as roughage such as beet pulp and brans are really not good roughage/fiber sources.) Some of the roughage will be broken down into substances the horse can absorb and use for calories and some of it will not. The correct amount of each type of fiber is important to the health of the intestines and will even influence his energy level, electrolyte levels and how well he can avoid dehydration.

Nondigestible Fiber

Nondigestible fiber is that portion that passes through the horse without being broken down and absorbed as a food. It is what we usually think of as bulk. Things like straw, tree bark, seed hulls, nut shells, wood and grasses eaten or made into hay at a late stage of maturity (after flowering and/or producing seed) are all very high in nondigestible fiber. These things obviously don't make much of a contribution to keeping weight on the horse but they do have a very important role in how well the intestines function.

The simplest explanation of why a horse needs nondigestible fiber is the term gut scratch factor.

These coarse materials fill the intestinal tract and stimulate it to contract. The muscular contractions of the intestine are important in mixing the contents and making sure that things keep moving along. Proper mixing guarantees that all foods get exposed to digestive enzymes and microorganisms inside the intestine and also that they will come in contact with the inner wall of the intestines, where absorption occurs.

The designation "fiber" on a feed bag does not necessarily tell you too much about how much gut scratch factor a feed has. The fiber portion of a ration refers to the percentage that will most likely make it through the stomach and small intestine without being digested. However, once it reaches the large intestine and begins to be acted on by the bacteria and protozoa that live there, some of that fiber will eventually be broken down and become available to the horse as a source of calories, vitamins and minerals.

Digestible Fiber

Digestible fiber is the fiber portion that the horse is capable of breaking down in his large intestine and using as a source of nutrients. It is possible for a food to have more fiber than grain but just as many or even more calories. Brans and beet pulp are the common higher fiber but also high-calorie feeds given to horses. The advantage over grain is they are digested in the large intestine and do not produce big jumps in blood sugar. (A high grain meal, especially corn, can raise blood sugar rapidly, like a candy bar.) They are also far less likely to produce changes in the acidity of the intestines that can kill beneficial organisms. Beet pulp is a good choice for horses with problems such as stable cough or heaves (respiratory system allergies) related to certain grains, hays or molds commonly contaminating those feeds (see Chapter Ten, Health Problems of the Older Horse). On the negative side, a horse not accustomed to these feeds may

Feed can contain a variety of ingredients such as cracked corn, sweet feed and whole oats.

bloat, become mildly uncomfortable and even have some loose manure or diarrhea if too much is fed at one time. They also have a large imbalance of calcium to phosphorus (too much calcium in beet pulp, the reverse for brans) that must be corrected by either supplements or the appropriate choices of hays and grains in the diet. (See Chapter Eleven, Managing the Very Old Horse.)

Bottom Line - Fiber

For proper digestion, the horse needs a minimum of 15% to 17% fiber in the diet. Grains contain 2% (corn, barley) to about 10% (oats) fiber; hays about 30% (alfalfa lower) and bran or beet pulp just over 10% fiber. If the horse has unlimited access to pasture or is eating at least 10 pounds of hay a day, you don't have to worry about fiber. Fiber becomes more of a concern for very old horses that can no longer eat hay (see Chapter Eleven.)

PROTEIN

Ask anyone what they are feeding their horse and if they use grain the first thing they will say is "x% protein." Everyone knows the protein content of their grain, but very few people know why it is important or what the overall protein content of their horse's diet (hay, pasture plus grain) is. Next time someone tries to tell you that a horse should always have a very low protein diet, remind them that fresh young grasses, the diet every horse does best on, are often over 20% protein!

It is widely held that too much protein is bad. Protein is critically important to the health of your horse. If you remove all the water from the horse's body and chemically analyze it, over 90% will be protein. The hoof wall, skin and coat are almost entirely protein. Improper protein content causes a much wider variety of health problems, many of them very serious, than does too few calories.

This does not mean the horse needs a lot of protein in his diet. It does mean that there must be enough and that the type of protein he is getting must be correct. Proteins are an assembly of small units called amino acids. Many of these amino acids the horse's body can put together itself using nitrogen molecules and sugars. Others he cannot manufacture and those must be present in the diet. These are called the essential amino acids. For other animals and people, research has identified eight, 10 or even more amino acids that are essential at all times or essential under certain conditions (serious illness/injury, heavy exercise, etc.). We know what they are and exactly how much the particular species must have in their diet for optimal growth and health. For the horse, we only have information on one essential amino acid—lysine. There are undoubtedly more—we just don't know what they are or how much the horse needs. For this reason, any protein recommendations made for horses are really

The average horse's diet is at least 75% carbohydrate, whether he eats grass or hay, gets grain or not. Here, two trail horses, Prince, 21, and Mirage, a 20-year-old palomino, stop to graze.

nothing more than educated guesses.

The average adult horse requires a minimum of about 10% protein in the diet. However, if the quality of the protein is poor (meaning it doesn't have a good variety of amino acids and/or is not absorbed particularly well), he will actually need more protein from that poor source to meet his needs. Researchers agree that older horses need high-quality protein to compensate for less efficient use of protein and less efficient absorption. For this reason, most commercial grain mixes formulated for older horses will contain a protein level closer to that recommended for pregnancy and growth than for idle mature horses; generally about 14%.

A target protein content of 14% is difficult to achieve with simple combinations of grains and hays.

High-quality alfalfa hays run about 17% protein according to the NRC, but grass hays and grains average only 10% or less. Feeding straight alfalfa will get you into trouble with mineral balances.

A better solution may be to do the best you can using a commercial high-quality grain mix and mixed alfalfa and grass hay (50:50) or grass hay only when making up the difference with small amounts of a high-quality protein supplement. (See sample diets and Chapter Four).

Bottom line: Adequate, quality protein is critical to the health of your older horse, both to prevent disease and to aid in his recovery from any disease or injuries. Just as important as providing adequate amounts of protein is making sure the protein comes from various sources. This is because the amino acid profile of the various hays and grains is different for each. By mixing sources, you stand a better chance of meeting all the horse's individual amino acid needs. Another way of accomplishing this, and one that I have found is particularly beneficial for young and older horses, is to add protein of a high biological quality. High biological quality simply means that the protein source has a wide variety of amino acids, is rich in essential amino acids and, most important, is very easily absorbed. Soybean is the premium protein usually added to horse feeds and it is the best of the vegetable proteins.

However, milk and egg protein, especially whey protein, beats soy hands down for biological quality. Supplementing with 40 to 60 grams of whey protein powder (available in any health store) can have a profound impact on health and appearance. It is particularly effective at boosting the immune response, a very important consideration for older horses. In fact, we now even have a supplement specifically for horses (GlutaSyn) that concentrates the immune-stimulating components of whey protein and has been proven to beneficially affect the immune cells.

The horse's coat, hoof quality, muscling and general vigor also benefit. When purchasing a whey protein from the health store for your horse, be sure to get one that specifies the protein is nondenatured. This simply means the important proteins have not been destroyed in the processing of the product. The total amount of protein does not have to be high, but the quality of it does. An overall protein content in the diet of 14% high-quality protein is advisable.

FAT

Fat has been a hot topic in equine nutrition lately. It has been touted as the cure to tying up and is used in large amounts to put weight on horses. It is also claimed to be the perfect energy source for endurance horses. Detailed discussion of all of this is outside the realm of this book, but a few comments on fat as it relates to the older horse are in order.

Fat, in limited amounts, is a useful addition to the horse's diet in some circumstances. However, the type of fat is important. You should know that the newer prilled (pelletized), dry fat products for horses are nothing more than processed lard (animal fat). They are not being promoted because they are good for your horse. They are being promoted because feeding them to horses gives meat processors a few extra dollars profit on something they would otherwise have to dispose of and gives manufacturers of equine supplements very cheap raw material to use in weight-gain products. Do not feed animal fat to your horse. Common sense alone should tell you it's not an appropriate thing to add to a horse's diet. They will eat it because it is so highly processed most won't know it's even in there. They will also absorb it and gain weight (fat) from it, but there are more healthful ways to accomplish this than feeding the horse lard.

A natural equine diet will contain only about 2% to 3% fat. That fat is derived from unprocessed seeds, beans and the heart (germ) of grains. These natural fat sources are very rich in fatty acids (fatty acids are the building blocks of fats, just like amino acids combine to

Meet Tuesday, a 23-year-old Anglo Arab owned by Cindy Foley of Warners, New York. In this spring picture, her trim and well-toned lines are evident. Tuesday has shown in the hunter ranks and fox hunted. A combination of light exercise, constant turn out and a high-quality diet has kept her in such good condition that she could easily pass for a horse 10 years younger.

form different proteins). We know from research in other species that there are essential fatty acids just like there are essential amino acids. Specifically, these are linoleic and linolenic acid. The chemistry of these fatty acids in the body is very complicated but boils down to the fact that, if the fatty acids are missing or imbalanced, the body chemistry will be shifted in a direction that favors inflammation. We have enough trouble trying to keep inflammation from strains, sprains, joint injury, muscle pulls, etc., under control without making

41

the job more difficult by feeding the horse the wrong type of fats. The essential fatty acids are also necessary for keeping the skin, coat and hooves healthy, shiny and supple. Dry skin, coat and feet are a dead giveaway that the horse is probably not getting enough essential fatty acids (although the vitamin biotin can be involved here, too). To complicate the picture, as the horse ages his ability to convert fatty acids into other forms used to manufacture hormones and anti-inflammatory substances decreases. Older horses have a higher requirement for the essential fatty acids.

The problem with getting fatty acids into the horse is that they break down very easily. In nature, the fatty acids are protected deep inside the seed/grain or bean that contains them and are not exposed to air or light. As soon as that protective shell is damaged (e.g., by rolling, crimping, cracking, etc.), the fatty acids begin to break down. In fact, the most sensitive indicator of high quality in oats is their fatty acid content. Oils extracted from these sources by pressing are a good concentrated source of essential fatty acids. Unfortunately, natural, cold-processed vegetable oils also will break down very quickly. To combat this problem, manufacturers use a process called heat stabilization. All this really means is that the essential fatty acids are largely destroyed by heat so that the end product will remain stable on the store shelf for a longer time. Feeding your horse liquid vegetable oils off the shelf is much better than prilled lard, but these oils are lacking the essential fatty acids the horse needs.

Oils also vary in the level of essential fatty acids they contain. Flax, pumpkin and soybean oils are the best sources of essential fatty acids, but only if they are not heat processed. You can tell immediately if a product has been heat processed by whether or not it needs to be refrigerated. Essential fatty acid rich products always need to be refrigerated. An exception to this is some raw-processed oils that still contain a good bit of sediment. The sediment is rich in vitamin E which protects the oils from breaking down. Cold-processed/raw oils can sometimes be purchased from bulk food manufacturers who supply the oil in this form to companies that heat-process and package it for store shelves. You may also be able to find raw/unprocessed oils in some supplement catalogs.

Powdered high-fat supplements are either animal fat or heat-processed high-fat rice bran. Neither of these has any significant fatty acid content. There is only one high fatty acid powdered product at this time, called Missing Link™ (Designing Health, Valencia, CA). This is a cold-processed product, primarily ground whole flax seed, that comes in a heavy foil, vacuum-sealed bag. Refrigeration after opening is suggested.

Bottom Line - Fats

The horse has a requirement for two essential fatty acids, normally derived from the heart/kernel/germ of seeds, beans and grains. The actual amount required in the diet is extremely small, probably about 4 to 6 tablespoons of the concentrated oil from these sources each day.

Any additional fat benefits the horse only in terms of high calories. Fat obtained from a high-fat grain mix, powdered fat supplement or liquid fat that is stable at room temperature will not contain the essential fatty acids. If your horse needs the extra calories, use a vegetable fat not an animal fat and preferably one that gives him health benefits as well—such as cold-processed flax seed or soybean oil or a cold-processed flax seed meal.

CARBOHYDRATES

The portion of the diet that remains after you subtract the content of fat, fiber and protein is carbohydrates. You will never see carbohydrate content listed on a feed bag but can figure it out easily enough by adding up the other three major categories and subtracting that

Diet does more than just keep the horse going. It's an important factor in health and performance.

from 100%. For example, a 5% fat, 10% fiber and 10% protein bag of grain will have 75% carbohydrates. (Carbohydrate % = 100% – (fat% + protein% + fiber%).

The average horse's diet is always at least 75% carbohydrate, whether he eats grass or hay; gets grain or not. However, not all carbohydrates are the same. Grains and fresh grass are more fattening because they contain more sugars and simple carbohydrates and much less fiber than hay. These break down in the intestine very easily to form glucose. Glucose is absorbed very quickly and efficiently in the small intestine and is what makes your horse's blood sugar go up after a meal. Unfortunately, if these sugars and simple carbohydrates are not fully absorbed and make their way back into the large intestine, they can cause digestive upset and alter the populations of beneficial bacteria and protozoa whose job it is to break down the digestible fiber portion of the diet. That is why feeding very large grain meals is not recommended and why it can make a horse seriously sick. Grass is not as likely to have this effect because the sugars and carbohydrates are much less concentrated in grasses than in grains. Grass contains three to five times as much water as hay or grains and, with the relatively small size of the horse's stomach, he is not going to be able to pack in as much carbohydrate from grass as he would from grain.

Bottom Line - Carbohydrates

The horse gets most of his calories in a natural diet from carbohydrates. However, grains and grasses have different forms of carbohydrate than do hays. Both grains and fresh green grass make the horse fatter because there is more easily digestible carbohydrate in them. Wheat bran, rice bran and beet pulp help prevent digestive problems caused by grain since more of their carbohydrate calories come from digestible fiber.

VITAMINS AND MINERALS

We have very little solid information on vitamin and mineral requirements in horses that comes from research actually done in horses, and even less when it comes to understanding the needs of the older horse. Chapter Four will deal with vitamin and mineral supplements for the older horse.

For the purposes of the basic diet, we need to look primarily at the major minerals—calcium, phosphorus, magnesium, potassium and salt (sodium and chloride).

Chart I (on page 51) lists the major minerals and how much of each the horse would obtain by eating 10 pounds of alfalfa, 10 pounds of timothy hay, five pounds of whole oats or 30 pounds of Kentucky bluegrass pasture. The 30 pounds of grass was used to allow for the much higher water content of grasses.

It is important that the horse's diet contain a least these individual total amounts and equally important that the amounts of minerals be maintained as close as possible to the ideal ratios of 1.2 to 1.5:1 for calcium:phosphorus and 2.6 to 2.0:1 for magnesium. A quick glance at this chart shows that potassium needs will be generously met by any diet that contains 10 pounds of hay or free access to pasture. Sodium and chloride (salt) needs cannot be met by any natural diet so the horse should always have access to plain white salt. (Trace mineral salt blocks are usually not balanced for horses and are not recommended.) Problems start to arise when you get into the numbers for calcium, phosphorus and magnesium. There's simply no way to make all total amounts correct and keep the mineral ratios where they should be using these natural feed sources.

BEST BASIC DIET FOR THE OLDER HORSE
Pasture

Man has yet to come up with any feed in a bag, or combination of hay and feed in a bag, that can duplicate the glow and good health shown by horses eating high-quality pasture as their only feed.

Horses on pasture receive high-quality protein which is probably also more digestible than grain, hay or soybean protein, easily digested carbohydrates and minerals in organic forms instead of the inorganic mineral salts added to most feeds (also more digestible). Because much of our information on requirements is based on experiments with the more artificial feeds of grains, hays and inor-

47

ganic mineral forms, it is difficult to even make a direct comparison between horses on fresh pasture and those on hay and grain. Compounding the problem is that pastures are rarely pure grasses of any type and horses are free to eat dirt, wildflowers, wild grasses—even tree bark—if they so desire. Fresh grass is also much easier to chew and contains a large amount of water to aid with good mixing and digestion in the intestines. Fresh grasses also contain essential fatty acids, vitamin C, other vitamins/antioxidants and complex sugars with important health benefits, such as immune stimulation. All are rapidly lost when grass is cut.

Bottom line is that the best diet for an older horse (or any horse for that matter) is fresh pasture, as much as he can eat. Horses do very well on all sorts of pasture types, and there are probably benefits to pastures that contain multiple types of grass and a selection of wildflowers as well.

Types that should be avoided are Sudangrass and Sudangrass-sorghum hybrids (can cause urinary, nervous system and reproductive problems), rye grass (dangerous fungi can grow in the feed stages, causing seizures, paralysis or death), the tropical grasses Dallis grass and Argentine Bahia grass (seizures) as well as kikuyu and setaria (interfere with calcium absorption), red clover (if infected with a certain fungus can cause excessive salivation), alsike clover (causes abnormal sensitivity to the sun) and tall fescue (dangerous for pregnant mares). The best pasture type is usually considered to be a mixture of grass that is suitable for the growing season in the area and a legume (alfalfa or clover). Alfalfa grown in the central area of the U.S. may be infested with blister beetles. These bugs contain a toxin that can kill horses even in relatively small amounts.

Commercial Senior Horse Feeds

Although we know that appropriate pasture is the perfect diet, very few horses are fortunate enough to have access to unlimited amounts of high-quality pasture all year round. The next best diet for the older horse is a high-quality commercial feed formulated especially for older horses.

These feeds contain additional major minerals, more absorbable trace minerals (see Chapter Four), higher percentage and quality of protein and usually have a higher fat content and calories in the form of beet pulp to help avoid large amounts of easily digestible carbohydrates causing upsets in the large colon. To see how a senior feed available in your area measures up, look for the following:

A. Can be fed as either a complete feed (no hay) or with hay. (This guarantees you will get the nutrition you need even if hay quality is very poor or hay not available. Also gives you the option of moistening the feed to a mash consistency for older horses with few teeth or other problems calling for a soft feed.)

B. Provides amounts of calcium and phosphorus listed in Chart 1 on page 51 requirements, when fed as directed for your horse's weight.

C. Trace minerals provided in an organic form (mineral name, e.g., copper or selenium, will be followed by one of these terms:

49

proteinate, methionine, lysine or polysaccharide complex).

D. Guaranteed levels of lysine and methionine on the bag in the analysis section.

E. List of ingredients contains milk or whey (highest quality protein sources).

F. Contains beet pulp in the list of ingredient.

Other Commercial Grain Mixes or Plain Grains and Hay

If you cannot find an appropriate senior formula feed in your area, your next best bet will probably be a 14% or 16% (depending on which is available) performance horse feed or mare and foal feed.

The requirements of the pregnant and growing horse, as well as the heavily worked horse, are similar to those of the older horse. Apply the same criteria listed in A through F above to these feeds. However, you will probably find that the mineral levels in the grain alone are not adequate, and it will be necessary to factor in the contribution from the hay or pasture your horse is getting.

The same is true when you are feeding plain grains and hay. The next chapter will walk you through this process.

Chart I

Natural Major Mineral Levels in Feeds (source NRC Nutrient Requirements of Horses, fifth Edition)

Feed	Calcium	Phosphorus	Magnesium	Potassium	Sodium	Chloride
Alfalfa *10 lbs.*	56.3	10.0	14.5	64.5	5.0	15.5
Timothy *10 lbs.*	19.5	9.0	5.5	73.1	0.5	N/A
Oats *5 lbs.*	1.6	7.0	2.9	8.2	1.0	1.8
Bluegrass Pasture Early Growth *30 lbs.*	0.5	19.1	6.8	95.5	5.5	19.1
Required Daily *(grams)*	27.3*	22.75***	10.2* to 13.7***	47.7	20.4	30.6

*Requirements listed for calcium, phosphorus and magnesium represent 150% of the suggested adult horse daily intake, 1,000 lb. body weight
** Usual suggested calcium:phosphorus ratio of 1.5:1 has been adjusted to 1.2:1 to allow for reported decreased efficiency of phosphorus absorption
*** A calcium:magnesium ratio of 2:1 (the higher magnesium recommendation) has been recommended by some authors, especially in working horses

CHAPTER FOUR

SUPPLEMENTS

Introduction

Young horses, like young people, can be active all day, show tremendous strength and work hard with minimal conditioning without waking up the next day feeling the effects. Sooner or later, though, the stiffness, aching and low energy levels we commonly associate with getting older begin to set in. Can we prevent this or at least push back aging?

According to theories on aging, there is both inevitable aging—probably largely genetic—and premature aging. Premature aging of horses—organs, bones, joints wearing out before their time—is caused by a combination of mechanical and outside influences such as poor conformation, speed work or any heavy exercise, infections, drugs and chemicals and the failure of the horse's body to completely repair the damage done. On the genetic front, the young animal has a surplus of healthy cells in all organs and structures. If they are only operating at 50% efficiency because of poor nutrition, it does not matter as much. If the load exceeds a cell's capacity, there are plenty more to pick up where that one left off. As the horse ages and number of active cells declines, it becomes increasingly important that they have all the nutrients they need to function effectively, neutralize the wastes they produce and repair any damage that might occur. This is where basic nutrition and appropriate supplementation comes in.

Traditionally, the focus in nutrition has been on the young horse and the pregnant mare. We agonize over getting the horse to the age of two or three but then tend to slack off with attention to nutrition, as if it is no longer as important. It is certainly true that nutritional inadequacies during the rapid growth and development phases can have consequences that will follow the horse throughout his life. However, it is also true that ignoring adequate (or better yet, optimal) nutrition in the adult years will rapidly result in premature aging.

There are also changes that occur in the animal's body with aging that call for different supplements/approaches to diet. In Chapter Three, we mentioned decreased efficiency of digestion and absorption. There are also chemical reactions inside the body that become less efficient with age and can result in health problems.

In Chapter Three we worked on building a sound basic diet but

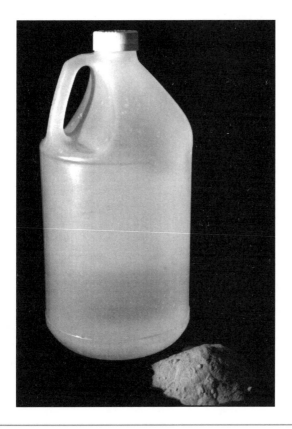

Brewer's Yeast may be used as a digestive enhancer to help liberate phosphorus inside fiber sources.

found there may be areas that need a little bolstering. There will also be specific problems that can benefit from supplementation of the diet. We will begin by taking at look at the major nutritional areas— digestion of food, fat, protein, fiber and major minerals—then proceed to vitamins and the trace minerals.

DIGESTION

The best diet in the world won't help the horse if it doesn't make its way into his bloodstream and body cells. This process begins at the mouth, where dental problems account for a large number of the appetite, digestion and weight loss problems of older horses.

Have your horse's teeth checked and worked on at least twice a year and any time he develops a change in appetite, change in eating patterns, decreased water consumption, weight loss, colic or change in manure or an unusual odor on the breath.

As the horse ages, the efficiency of digestion (breaking down foods into chemicals the bloodstream can absorb) lessens. There are many factors involved in this including digestive enzymes and hormones, acid secretion in the stomach, how well the muscular walls of the intestine contract, how well the cells lining the intestine can absorb nutrients and the health of the microorganisms in the large bowel, which are responsible for breaking down much of the plant material the horse eats, are involved in mineral absorption and also manufacture B vitamins the horse can absorb and use.

Digestive Enzymes: There are some feeds and supplement products that claim to contain digestive enzymes. This sometimes refers to enzymes produced by or contained in bacteria or yeast. These will appear on an ingredients list as fermentation byproducts. Otherwise, a look at the ingredients list usually reveals there are enzymes obtained from plant sources, like bromelain or papain. How much they help the horse's digestion is anyone's guess. As far as we know, they don't do any harm. Until we know more, the best advice is not to buy a product, or pay extra, just because the label claims digestive enzymes.

Digestive Enhancers: There are several different things that go under the category of digestive enhancers.

A. Yeast: Live yeast cultures or yeast fermentation products can be found in many commercial feeds and supplements. Yeasts in the large intestine of the horse assist in the breakdown of plant materials and help to liberate the minerals inside those fiber sources. Yeast may be added as live cultures or as yeast fermentation products (these encourage the growth of yeast in the intestines). The source may be Brewer's yeast or a specific species such as YeaSacc (a brand name), Aspergillus oryzae or Saccharomyces cerevisiae. Caution: Some horses do not like the smell and/or taste of yeast and will take quite a while to accept products containing it, if they ever do. Some will also develop digestive upset such as bloating and increased gas from yeast. If this occurs, stop using products containing live yeast cultures. Fermentation products alone usually do not have these side effects.

B. Probiotics: The term probiotics usually refers to beneficial bacteria but some products include yeast as well. Products may include only one type of bacteria (usually a Streptomyces species), one type of fermentation product from a bacteria, or mixes of many bacteria. Probiotics may be in a special probiotic product or can even be mixed into grains by special technology that encapsulates the live bacteria in a shell that is only broken by digestive enzymes in the stomach. The inclusion of beneficial digestive bacteria and fermen-tation products in feeds or supplements is definitely a plus for the older horse. Feed efficiency improves, grains disappear from the manure, etc. I recommend them highly.

FATS

One of the most important aging changes involves dealing with fats. The horse's actual requirement for fats is very low (see Chapter Three). He does need them, however, to produce powerful body chemicals like hormones and prostaglandins. We've all heard about fats and weight gain, fats and heart disease. What you don't hear too much about is how the type of fats eaten influences such things as health of the skin and hair, arthritis and inflammation. The horse needs a certain level of the essential fatty acids (essential meaning they must be provided by the diet; the horse can't make them him-self) to keep the hormones and inflammatory chemicals in balance. As he ages, this becomes even more important since he begins to lose the ability to change some of these essential fatty acids into other fatty acid forms. He is no longer able to get by with shortages without showing symptoms.

Processing oils to make them stable enough to keep at room temperature essentially destroys the fatty acids. Grains that normally have a good fatty acid level, like oats, lose it rapidly if they are crimped or rolled. It is a good idea to provide the older horse with a source of essential fatty acids. All it will take is about 1/3 cup of cold-processed flaxseed meal or six tablespoons of flaxseed oil. Remember, if you don't see instructions on the label that the product has to be refrigerated, don't buy it. There aren't enough fatty acids in there to do the horse any good. There are a few joint products and rice bran supplements out there that claim to provide essential fatty acids. Don't believe them. The levels were good before the product was processed, but by the time it reaches you they are all but gone.

PROTEIN

The best and easiest way to get adequate protein into your older or getting older horse is to choose a high-quality commercial grain mix and use only top-quality hay. A good 12% grain mix will be adequate if you feed alfalfa, or at least 25% alfalfa, or if the horse is on lush spring/fall pastures.

Otherwise, use a 14% protein grain mix. The best-quality grains will list milk or whey on their label ingredients list. Alfalfa meal would be the next best protein source in a grain mix, at least in terms of amino acid variety and ease of digestion. However, soybean meal and other soybean products are by far the most commonly used protein supplement in grain mixes. When properly processed, soybean is rich in lysine, the only amino acid in the horse's diet we have much solid information about. Soybean can cause digestive upsets in any horse, especially the older horse. If your horse has a big belly (often called a hay belly), excessive gas or signs of mild colic, try him on a soybean-free diet, such as plain oats, for a week or so. If the symptoms go away, suspect soybean as the culprit. A soy-sensitive horse can be fed plain grains (e.g., oats alone, oats and corn if he has trouble holding his weight) and can be supplemented with a protein powder from your local drugstore or health store. (Even this will not be necessary if he is getting about 50% alfalfa hay and high-quality, plump oats.) Horses digest either milk protein, whey protein or milk and egg protein powders extremely well. An added benefit is that the quality of these protein powders is so high you can feed much less. I have seen horses benefit from as little as 40 to 60 grams of milk, whey or milk/egg powder per day.

Symptoms of protein deficiency include loss of muscle mass (not reliable in older horses unless they are being regularly exercised), poor-quality hooves, slow growth rate of hooves and hair, rough hair coat, dry skin, frequent skin or respiratory infections. Protein stimulates the immune system.

MAJOR MINERALS

The major minerals of concern are calcium, phosphorus and magnesium. In Chapter Three we list recommended levels for total intake from all sources—diet and supplements. These levels will be difficult to achieve from your grains and hays alone. Table IV-1 on page 70 lists recommended supplement levels for various diets. It is always wise to have your hay analyzed for mineral levels before supplementing. Levels will vary widely from area to area and even within an area in different years. The numbers used here are based on average analyses performed by the National Research Council but may bear little resemblance to what it is in the hay you feed. If the horse is being maintained on good pasture only, it is imperative you have it analyzed. Cost is only about $20 in most areas. You cannot determine supplements needed until you have this done, since a wide variety of plants and grass types in the field may contribute to the mineral picture. For example, a timothy pasture will contain all the major minerals the older horse needs, but a bluegrass pasture may need heavy supplementation.

To sample a pasture properly, mix cut grasses and plants taken from all areas of the pasture where the horses frequently graze. (Cut off about 1/2 above ground level.) As you walk around you will see there are spots they hardly seem to graze at all. These might be areas of different soil type or areas where manure has built up. Whatever the cause, don't bother sampling these grasses and plants because odds are the horses will let them get several feet high, eat off everything else and still won't touch them!

Potassium will be present in adequate amounts in the diet of any horse that eats hay or pasture. Sodium and chloride (plain salt) is never present in adequate amounts and should always be available to the horse as a plain salt block (white salt). The last major mineral in the body is sulfur. The horse's body definitely requires sulfur but more than likely cannot absorb or use it well in mineral form. His sulfur comes from proteins in the feeds that contain this mineral. Sulfur needs will be met when the horse gets adequate high-quality protein.

TRACE/MINOR MINERALS

The trace minerals are copper, zinc, manganese, iodine and selenium. Cobalt is also included but is virtually always present in adequate amount. They are called trace or minor minerals because the amount needed is small compared to something like calcium. However, a deficiency of any one of them is guaranteed to cause a variety of problems—anything from arthritis or tying-up to hormone imbalances.

IRON AND THE OLDER HORSE

Iron in any form is not only unnecessary but potentially harmful, especially for older horses.

Horses get and very efficiently absorb all the iron they need for any sort of diet, even one of poor-quality feeds and hays. They also are very good at recycling the iron that is already in their body.

In fact, there has never been a single case of diet-related iron deficiency in a horse. Too much iron can destroy fragile vitamins in the diet (Bs and C) and adds to the free radical burden in the body, something an older horse definitely does not need. It will be difficult to find a feed or supplement that does not have added iron but if you do, use it. Otherwise, check labels carefully and choose supplements that contain the least amount of iron. Iron citrate, a buffered iron, is better than iron sulfate.

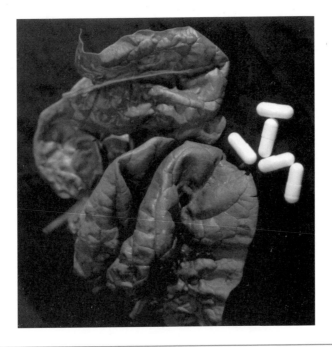

Supplemental iron in any form is not only unnecessary, but can be potentially harmful, especially for older horses.

Vitamin C

It is true that horses can manufacture their own supply of vitamin C in their bodies. It is also true that horses do not develop the classic vitamin C deficiency disease, scurvy, which is basically a breakdown of bones, tendons and all connective tissues since the body cannot form these properly without vitamin C. Because of these two facts, it is usually said that horses do not need vitamin C in their diet. They may not need it to stay alive and free of scurvy, but more and more people

Feeding vitamin C to horses may seem strange if it makes you think of oranges and lemons, which horses don't like. However, consider that a pound of fresh grass contains as much as 500 mg of vitamin C.

believe they do indeed need it for maximal health and this is especially true of older horses. Recent studies have shown that older horses have lower levels of vitamin C in their blood, and vitamin C is becoming a common addition to feeds formulated for older horses and to all horse feeds and supplements.

If feeding vitamin C to horses still sounds strange because it makes you think of oranges and lemons—not exactly the horse's favorites—consider this. One pound of fresh grass can contain as much as 500 mg of vitamin C. A horse getting all his nutrition from live grasses probably consumes at least 20 to 30 pounds of grass per day. That's a lot of vitamin C. In contrast, hay and grains have essentially zero vitamin C content. We all know which is the more natural diet.

Not too surprisingly, research has shown it takes a minimum of 4.5 grams of vitamin C (the equivalent of nine pounds of grass) to even make a change in a horse's vitamin C level. A minimum effective level is probably more like seven grams. Every older horse should receive at least this level of vitamin C per day, which will mean you need to use a supplement containing C. Even vitamin C-supplemented grains don't come close to this level. A patented, buffered form of vitamin C (easier on the digestive tract) is available, called Ester-C™. However, most horses, even older horses, tolerate plain vitamin C very well.

B VITAMINS

Table I lists the individual B vitamins and the recommended level of supplementation. The horse is only partially dependent on the level of B vitamins in his foods since the organisms that live in his intestinal tract also make them and the horse can use this source. However, as with vitamin C, it is not safe to assume that this means the horse never would benefit from additional B vitamins.

This is especially true for older horses, whose intestinal tracts are not as strong and vigorous as a young animal's. There is not a single cell in the horse's body, a single body function, a single organ that does not absolutely require B vitamins to function. The horse also needs B vitamins on a daily basis since his body cannot store them.

Many of the B vitamins require other B vitamins to be activated or as cofactors in performing their functions in the body. For this reason, it is always recommended that Bs be supplemented as a balanced group in the basic diet. Supplemental B vitamins often give the horse a general sense of well being and are effective at stimulating the appetite. The B vitamins are also important in maintaining the blood counts/preventing anemia. There are also specific health problems that might call for increased levels of one or more B vitamins and these will be discussed in Chapter Ten and other chapters that deal with specific health problems. A well-known example of this is the use of additional Biotin supplements to treat horses with problems of their skin, coat and/or hooves.

THE FAT SOLUBLE VITAMINS

Vitamins A, D, E and K are the fat soluble vitamins. They get this name from the fact that can enter and be stored in body fat. They are commonly found in high levels in the liver and kidney.

Vitamin K is one vitamin that you don't have to worry about supplementing. Only horses with liver failure severe enough to threaten their lives ever have abnormally low vitamin K levels.

A, D and E however must be obtained from the diet or by synthesis in the body. Vitamin D is the sunshine vitamin. The horse manufactures D when he is exposed to sunlight. Oversupplementation of vitamin D can easily cause toxic reactions so you must be careful to tally up all sources of vitamin D in the diet—grains and supplements—and not to overdo it. A and E must come from the diet. Vitamin E is an important antioxidant that protects the membranes surrounding cells and structures inside cells from damage. Vitamin E is in short supply in most diets and supplementation is recommended. Toxicity from vitamin E is at least theoretically possible, but no one has ever described it actually happening. Vitamin A is important for protection and function of the skin, respiratory tract, urinary tract and reproductive tract. It is an important antioxidant in people, where it helps protect from heart disease and hardening of the arteries. The antioxidant roles of vitamin A in the horse are less well understood but consequences of vitamin A deficiency in skin, bone, the eyes and other organs are well described. Grains contain little or no vitamin A, and hays rapidly lose it when they lose their bright green color (good alfalfa has plenty of vitamin A, but pale grass hays are often deficient). Because the functions of vitamin A and symptoms of deficiency are so well known, many manufacturers tend to go a little overboard when they add it to their supplements. As with vitamin D, always be sure to total up the amount of vitamin A the horse is getting from all sources and do not overdose it.

Vitamin A can be toxic to vital organs.

OTHER SUPPLEMENTS

There are many, many other supplements available for horses—far too many to list them all here.

Vitamin cofactors (things that help vitamins work better), include medicinal herbs, phytochemicals, phytohormones, enzymes, metabolic intermediates. These are all terms you might hear in connection with an equine supplement. This book will cover many other classes of supplements in the chapters on dealing with specific problems of the older horse.

FOODS AS DRUGS

We are conditioned to think of drugs as good things. They get rid of pain, kill bacteria or tumor cells, chemically jumpstart hearts that are not working properly, even fix negative moods or bad thoughts. Drugs are an indispensable part of medicine and, when properly used, important weapons in the fight against many diseases. However, it is important to remember that with very few exceptions drugs do not cure the disease, and without exception drugs do not correct the weakness that allowed the disease to appear in the first place. You do not treat/cure arthritis with phenylbutazone or colic with Banamine ™.

These drugs only block the pain. The underlying disease continues despite them. Drugs that do actually treat always come with a price tag. Antibiotics kill harmful bacteria but beneficial ones as well, leaving the horse susceptible to colic and yeast/fungal infections. Antibiotics can also be toxic to organ systems such as the nervous system or muscles. Chemotherapy drugs kill tumor cells but also damage or kill a wide variety of the normal cells in the body. A dose of acepromazine may take the edge off that always nervous and jumpy horse so that you can ride him but tomorrow you will be faced with the same problem.

Proteins, vitamins, minerals—the basic building blocks of the body and every system in it—may be far more potent drugs than anything sitting on a pharmacy shelf. Without them, disease, degeneration and infection set in rapidly and the damage caused cannot be repaired. One of the most effective treatments for the common cold anyone has yet to come up with is a simple combination of zinc and vitamin C. Thiamine (a B vitamin) and magnesium (a simple mineral) have done more to safely, effectively and permanently change nervous and supersensitive horses into normal, sane and functional mounts than any tranquilizing drug. Naturally occurring simple body chemicals can work near miracles in actually curing diseases or revers-

→

68

ing their effects. Chondroitin sulfate and glucosamine can rebuild joint cartilage destroyed by arthritis. CoQ10, an antioxidant manufactured in the body whose levels decline with age, can increase the exercise capacity of people with heart disease by as much as 50%, ease the work of breathing in chronic lung disease and make a sluggish older horse feel like he's years younger.

We are all conditioned to want a shot or a pill when our horse is injured or not feeling well. These things do have their place in managing the consequences of disease, injury or illness. Remember though, that the fact we are reaching for a drug means that the body has failed and very often an important factor in that failure is inadequate nutrition. It is just as important to identify and correct any contributing nutritional causes as it is to control symptoms. If you don't, the horse will have a much more difficult time repairing the damage and preventing the problem in the future.

TABLE IV – 1
RECOMMENDED SUPPLEMENT LEVELS
CHART 1-A

MAJOR AND TRACE MINERALS, AMOUNTS FROM ALL SUPPLEMENTS

	Ca	Ph	Mag	Zi	Cu	Mn	Se	Io
25:75 Alfalfa/Grass Hay	0	6g	0 * for total mag only	150 mg	75 mg	150 mg	1 mg	1 mg
25:75 Alfalfa/Grass Hay w/Plain Grain, 5 lb/day	0	12g	0-3g * for total mag only	=	=	=	=	=
25:75 Alfalfa/Grass Hay w/Commercial Grain, 5 lb/day	0	0	0* for total mag only	0-75 mg	0-40 mg	0-75 mg	0	0

MAJOR AND TRACE MINERALS, AMOUNTS FROM ALL SUPPLEMENTS

	Ca	Ph	Mag	Zi	Cu	Mn	Se	Io
Grass Hay Only	0	6g	0-3 g* total only	150 mg	75 mg	150 mg	1-2 mg	1-2 mg
Grass Hay w/Plain Grain, 5 lb/day	8g	7.5g	2-5g	"	"	"	"	"
Grass Hay w/Commercial Grain, 5 lb/day	0 total	0 total	0* for mag only	0-75 mg	0-40 mg	0-75 mg	1 mg	1 mg
Good Pasture Only	4g	7g	2-5g	0	0	0	1 mg	1 mg

NOTE: Commercial grain mix, senior or young/pregnant horse type, 14% to 16% protein. Pasture must be highest quality, unlimited. Using high-quality midbloom hay or late vegetative pasture, grass/pasture type Timothy. Amounts given do not take into account corrections to bring Ca:P or Ca:Mg ratios into ideal range.

71

CHART 1-B

VITAMINS – TOTAL AMOUNTS FROM ALL SUPPLEMENTS

	Thiamine	Riboflavin	Niacin	Panto-thenic Acid	Pyri-doxine
25:75 alfalfa/grass hay	150mg	125	180	20	20
25:75 alfalfa/grass hay 5# plain grain	75	60	90	10	10
25:75 alfalfa/grass hay 5# commercial grain	75	60	90	10	10
grass hay	150	125	180	20	20
grass hay 5# plain grain	75	60	90	10	10
grass hay 5# commercial grain	75	60	90	10	10
good pasture - unlimited	75	60	90	10	10

Cyanoco-balamin	Biotin	Folic Acid	Vitamin A	Vitamin D	Vitamin C	Vitamin E
0	2.5	2	up to 20,000IU	up to 2,000IU	5g	1,000IU
0	1	1	up to 20,000IU	up to 2,000IU	5	1,000IU
0	1	1	up to 10,000IU	up to 1,000IU	5	1,000IU
0	2.5	2	up to 40,000IU	up to 2,000IU	5	1,000IU
0	1	1	up to 40,000IU	up to 2,000IU	5	1,000IU
0	1	1	up to 20,000IU	up to 1,000IU	5	1,000IU
0	1	1	0	0	0	0

CHAPTER FIVE

DEALING WITH
ENVIRONMENTAL
TOXINS

CHEMICALS, THE INVISIBLE THREAT

Your horse doesn't have to be grazing over a landfill to be exposed to dangerous chemicals. For example, Dioxin, the most potent toxin yet known, is everywhere. The Environmental Protection Agency (EPA) says that all Americans harbor this toxic chemical and the most likely significant source is meat in the diet. There are 75 known toxic forms of Dioxin, which is but one of a slew of chemicals already contaminating the air, land and water. A safe cumulative lifetime exposure to TCDD (a dangerous Dioxin) as estimated by the EPA amounts to a weight of no more than 1/9,900,000 grains of salt, a level that makes it one million times more toxic than arsenic. In Times

$\longrightarrow$

Beach, Missouri (population 2,800), Dioxin-contaminated oil was sprayed on the roads in the 1970s to keep the dust down. When the EPA sampled the area some 10 years later, Dioxin levels of less than 1 to 127 ppb (parts per billion) were found, sufficient to order evacuation of the town, which remains deserted to this day. Dioxin contamination of Agent Orange is believed responsible for the health problems of many Viet Nam veterans. Dioxin and thyroxin are also chemical cousins. The major source of Dioxin and the related family of compounds is from plastics and pesticides, but they are released in lesser amounts from other sources, including the bleaching of paper. A recent study found women with breast cancer have 50% to 60% higher levels of PCBs in their breast tissue than normal women. This, and other microscopic amounts of toxic chemicals, exist everywhere. In December of 1998 it was reported that PCN, a precursor of the highly toxic PCBs (polychlorinated biphenyls), which have Dioxin-like toxicities, was detected in the air over the Arctic Circle.

ATRAZINE

Even the chemicals in wide use on our fields pose a health threat to your horse (and you). Atrazine is an herbicide that has been banned by several countries but is still the most widely used in the U.S. and Canada. Seventy-five million pounds of this weed-killing stuff is dumped on cornfields annually. It persists in soil and water supplies for over a year and was the second most frequently detected contaminant in an EPA well water survey. If your horses are located close to cornfields, odds are the prevailing winds are carrying this chemical over to your pastures and ponds, and from there into your well water. Even short-term exposure above the EPA's Maximum Contaminant Level of three parts per billion has been reported to cause congestion of the lungs, heart and kidney, low blood pressure, muscle spasms, weight loss and damage to the adrenal glands. Long-term exposure causes weight loss, muscle and eye damage, heart damage and cancer including cancers of the reproductive organs, leukemia and lymphoma. Remember, standard well water testing does not look for this type of chemical. If you suspect a problem, collect a sample of your water sources and the pasture right after the nearby fields were sprayed and call the state office of the Environmental Protection Agency. If they won't help, ask where you can pay to get it tested yourself.

76

THE PROBLEM – AN OVERVIEW

The world around us is changing so rapidly we tend to forget that many of the things we view as familiar and routine really haven't been around very long. Those vaccines your horse has received have been around for less than 40 years. Many people still remember polio epidemics, even know someone who had the disease. It wasn't until the late '40s and early '50s (first Plexiglas sign, first plastic records) that the boom in plastic manufacture began to occur. Tupperware and those ubiquitous plastic lawn chairs first appeared in 1951. Pesticides to kill the bugs and herbicides to destroy unwanted weeds and ground cover in lawns and cultivated fields have been used since the 1920s but it was the research into chemical warfare during World Wars I and II that led to the explosion in these chemicals' agricultural use; first DDT in the '40s, then the organophosphates in the '50s and '60s. The type of research and development that eventually produced these chemicals should have been our first clue that their use could have dire consequences. Remember the days when you had to fast your horse for 12 hours before he could be tubed with that wormer that even then could cause colic and founder? The drug used was an organophosphate and millions of gallons of very similar stuff are sprayed on the fields where your horse's grain and hay is grown every year.

Electronics, energy generation, automobile manufacturing, refining, paper products—virtually any industry you can think of has its own collection of toxic wastes. The industrial revolution has been with us for a long time but the tremendous boom in industry did not occur until after World War II. Early prophets of the price to be paid, such as Rachel Carson, author of *Silent Spring*, were ridiculed and dismissed as alarmists or environmental radicals. While your horse may not drop over after a mouthful of pesticide-sprayed hay, these and other environmental chemicals are stored in the body for prolonged periods, in the fat and vital organs such as the liver or kidneys. As levels rise over time, health problems begin to develop. It takes 20+ years of low level exposure for any ill effects to be seen. Even then, diseases may be diagnosed but no thought given to the underlying cause.

Hypothyroidism is among the most common disorders of aging people. Thyroxine, the equine equivalent being Thyrol L, is the #1 prescription in the United States. Decreased fertility (especially in males), hypothyroidism and abnormalities of the uterine lining have climbed steadily as health problems in people at a rate that parallels the chemical toxin Dioxin. Concerns over hypothyroidism in horses are also on the rise as more and more owners complain about lack of energy, weight problems, abnormal fat deposits and skin/coat problems in their horses that seem to have no explanation. A 1996 paper in the *Canadian Veterinary Journal* reported a link between foals born with hypothyroidism and immature skeletal structures and mares that had grazed on pastures or drank from natural water sources contaminated with high levels of nitrates—the commonly used nitrogen fertilizer. Water nitrate levels in my heavily agricultural area are so high people often cannot use their natural well water

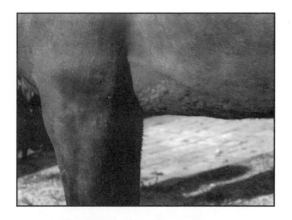

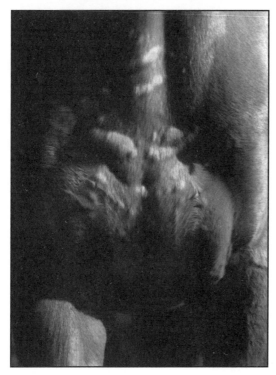

Skin problems, such as hives, may be the result of exposure to pollution.

without getting sick, infants need bottled water for their formulas (bottled water is tested for nitrates; local water testing authorities don't) but horses drink this stuff all the time. Many other chemicals can also affect the thyroid. It doesn't take much thought to see a possible link between the unexplained problems of hypothyroidism and increasing exposure to these substances.

Altered thyroid function in turn effects the immune system. One of the horse's best defenses against infectious disease is fever. On a day-to-day basis, however, most of the organisms the horse comes in contact with never gain a foothold because the horse's normal body temperature is not suitable for their growth. What happens if the horse's body temperature becomes lower because his thyroid is not functioning properly? It opens the door for a host of infections that would otherwise normally never bother a horse. Low-grade but persistent skin infections appear, often with a fungal component. (Those little crusty patches that come off with a few hairs attached.) Poorly described and equally persistent respiratory problems increase.

Even more serious organisms can also gain a hold and do massive damage, like EPM-equine protozoal myelitis.

The horse's immune system itself can also be damaged by a very wide range of chemicals. In addition to the problems with infections, immune-related cancers can occur. Non-Hodgkin's lymphoma, a collection of immune cell (T and B cell) cancers in people, is rising at an alarming rate. Horses in general are not very prone to developing malignant diseases (cancers) but lymphoma/lymphosarcoma is also one of the few cancers they do get, especially

The incidence of respiratory problems and lung weakening is growing in high-pollution areas.

older horses. One of the highest human risk groups for this cancer is farmers. Exposure to herbicides and pesticides is high on the list of suspected causes. The types of cells found under the microscope in these tumors is changing. It is probably no coincidence that scientific reports of exactly the same cell types in lymphomas from horses are just beginning to appear.

There are other subtle indicators that our horses' body chemistries are being negatively affected by substances in the modern world. Asthma is rising at an epidemic rate in people and horses. Highly stressed horses especially are at great risk for developing all sorts of respiratory problems and lung weakening, particularly those that are kept in high-pollution areas such as at racetracks close to large cities. Groups of horses may be affected by pollution, like the report from Ireland of a farm where skin problems, reproductive problems, respiratory problems and a relatively rare intestinal disorder that is like Crohn's disease in people (an autoimmune disease—the body attacks its own tissue) was found in a herd of horses exposed to high levels of aluminum and other environmental toxins. Stomach ulcers are also on the rise, to the point that a large drug company has just this year gone to the trouble and expense of having one of the human anti-ulcer drugs approved for horses. The rise in reports of ulcers is not just because of improved diagnosis.

If stomach ulcers had been a problem all along they would have been described as common findings in pathology books. A 1980s edition of *Equine Medicine and Surgery*, a primary textbook in veterinary schools, does not even mention stomach ulcers. Stallions with low sperm counts, mares which do not cycle normally or cannot hold a pregnancy are common problems. If it was always this difficult to get mares in foal, the species would have died out long ago. The combination of stress (like aging), altered body chemistry and the effects of toxins on specific body organs is slowly but surely changing the profile of diseases we can expect to see in our horses.

What To Do

You can't fight the entire industrial world or shield your horse from toxic substances that might find their way into his food and water, even the air. What you can do is at least be aware of the problem and

On a practical level, one way to begin fighting pollution is to get effective water treatment.

take any chance you get to voice an opinion or vote as you should on the issue. There is no cure for the damage these chemicals can do, no drug that will reverse their effects.

On a practical level, begin with getting effective water treatment. Municipal (city) water can be contaminated with a broad range of harmful chemicals, some of which (like chlorine and aluminum) may have been deliberately added. You should also be aware that if a problem is discovered with your municipal water, many cities have 72 hours to correct it before they are required to notify the public. Meanwhile, you and your horse are drinking the water. Well water poses its own special hazards from heavy metals, fertilizers and herbicides. Water-softening units only remove calcium and magnesium from the water. They do nothing for most toxic metals and chemicals. There are water treatment units available today that can handle these problems. They are called reverse osmosis systems and usually come with ultraviolet treatment as well, to kill bacteria in the water.

Avoid grazing your horse on fields that have been chemically treated, including your front yard. Before putting down any fertilizer or other treatment, take a soil and vegetation sample to your state agricultural extension agent and ask for an analysis and suggestions. Pay attention to your horse's water sources. Test them as carefully as you would your own—even more carefully than routine water testing that usually concentrates on levels of bacteria. Test kits for nitrates are relatively easy to obtain, or you can send the sample to a water-testing lab in your area (check the phone book). Tests for individual pesticides, herbicides and other chemicals are extremely expensive and there are hundreds of potential contaminants. However, you may be able to obtain information on this by contacting the EPA or your state environmental protection office. The EPA has an amazing storehouse of data and, if you are having problems, may be willing to get involved.

Closer to home, the best way to combat the effects of toxic minerals and chemicals is to fight back with dietary adjustments that will correct the horse's body chemistry and compete with the harmful substances for absorption. Forward-thinking supplement companies

There are many supplements available for horses that contain needed vitamins and minerals.

such as Uckele Health and Nutrition (Blissfield, MI) and Vita-Royal (Davison, MI) are developing lines of products that protect the horse's intestinal tract from the effects of toxins and restore normal intestinal health. Making sure the horse is getting adequate amounts of high-quality minerals, both major minerals and trace minerals, in his diet corrects deficiencies, fuels the detoxification mechanisms of his body and competes with the toxic substances for absorption. High-quality protein, particularly whey protein, will help keep his immune system and hormonal systems functioning at their best, as will providing essential fatty acids on a daily basis. Use of antioxidant vitamins and supplements (vitamin C, bioflavinoids, vitamin E, grape seed extract, CoQ10) will also combat much of the toxicity and cell damage that can result from environmental toxins. If a thyroid supplement is needed, ask your veterinarian to order you the natural thyroid gland extract from Eudaemonics or use a thyroid support system such as the one available from Uckele Health and Nutrition. Natural immune system boosters such as garlic, Echinacea and the very recently discovered arabanogalactin sugars, when fed regularly, are very beneficial and older horses seem to be particularly sensitive to their effects.

There are no drugs to prevent or treat the underlying toxicities, only drugs that may temporarily alleviate the symptoms while leaving the cause unaffected. The environmental toxins go to the core of your horse's chemistry to do their damage. The only way to combat this and repair the injury/dysfunction is to fight fire with fire. Provide the horse's body with what it needs to get functioning normally again and symptoms will disappear because the horse is cured. However, this must be an approach you maintain for the rest of the horse's life. Once you see the improved level of health, you may not want to stop.

TABLE 5-1

SIGNS AND SYMPTOMS OF CHEMICAL AND/OR MINERAL TOXICITY

Poor stress tolerance
- easily put off feed by any stress
- hard to bring to top form and does not hold top form

Weight problems
- either abnormal fat deposits or too thin (breed, exercise and complicated hormonal factors probably operating)

Erratic body temperature

Vague skin problems
- flaking/seborrhea may be most noticeably manifested as tail rubbing and flaking skin on tail
- sensitivity to topical chemicals (body washes, liniments, alcohol, etc.)
- low-grade bacterial or fungal infections common

Coat problems
- hair does not lay flat/sleek
- grayish hue to skin
- brittle mane and tail
- reddish/rusty discoloration to black hair
- slow to shed out
- hair growth/regrowth (e.g., in clipped areas) slow

Foot problems
- scratches
- vesicles along coronary band (severe cases)

- splitting, cracking, quarter cracks
- tender footed (may be low-grade laminitis in many cases)

Abnormal skin sensitivity to light touch

Myofascial pain with multiple trigger points
- resting muscle tone usually abnormally high

History of tying-up

GI
- picky appetite for grain
- intolerant of feed changes
- prone to abdominal bloating
- soy and alfalfa intolerance (just a handful of a high soy supplement like Calf Manna or Equine soy based product will bloat them up)
- constipation or prone to intermittent diarrhea, especially when stressed (e.g., trailering)
- may be prone to mild colic

Hypoglycemia (common)

Documented or suspected hypothyroidism

Suspected adrenal dysfunction
- stress intolerance as above
- electrolyte abnormalities with chronic, low-grade dehydration
- abnormal sweating (pattern and/or amount)

Sexual dysfunction
- low libido in stallions
- low sperm counts
- abnormal estrus cycles
- short or long periods of estrus
- abnormal interval between estrus periods
- difficulty conceiving
- early fetal losses

History of allergic-type symptoms
- skin sensitivities including severe reaction to insect bites, iodine sensitivity common
- respiratory
- chronic nasal discharge - clear to whitish
- stable cough
- lymphoid hyperplasia of pharynx in young horses

- recurrent infections
- heaves
- multiple feed intolerances

Behavior
- may be dull or very anxious
- lack of usual interest in barn activities; stand in the back of their stalls
- frequent vocalization
- aggressive/antisocial
- for lack of better description, these horses are just not happy; you can see it in their eyes

Arthritis/synovitis in multiple joints—often out of proportion to the age of the animal and/or amount of pounding he has been subjected to—and/or history of shifting leg lameness that defies diagnosis, stiffness
- some of these will turn out to be EPM but have also seen it in horses that show no clear neurological signs

Laboratory abnormalities may include:
- elevated muscle enzymes
- borderline to frankly low magnesium
- low serum CO_2/acidosis
- low normal red cell counts with normal indices
- low normal to low thyroid function tests (usually T4, T3 levels very erratic)—high performance animals most likely to actually show this
- hypokalemia (low blood potassium)
- hypoglycemia (40s and 50s) (low blood sugars)

TABLE 5-2

SUGGESTED BASIC DIET AND SUPPLEMENT PROGRAM FOR HORSES WITH SYMPTOMS OF ENVIRONMENTAL DISEASE

Plain grains or top-of-the-line commercial feed*, 14% to 16% protein, and high-quality grass hay (use plain grains only for horses with history of digestive tract bloating or hay belly) No extruded or pelleted feeds
Non-denatured whey protein powder 40 g/day (up to 80 for horses in poor condition)
Cold-processed flax seed oil 6 tablespoons or cold-processed flax seed meal 1/3 to 1/2 cup/day

Magnesium-based intestinal tract buffer such as Nutrient Buffer[R]
from Vita-Royal
Probiotic and gut-protective factors such as G.U.T.™ from Uckele Health and
Nutrition for horses with history of ulcers or digestive tract problems like bloating

- Magnesium 3 to 8 g/day
- Vitamin C 10 g/day
- Vitamin E 2,000 IU/day
- Selenium 2 mg/day (as selenomethionine, not sodium selenite)
- Zinc minimum 200 mg/day (not zinc sulfate, use zinc chelates or poly-saccharide trace minerals)
- Copper minimum 75 mg/day (not sulfate, use chelates or polysaccharide trace minerals)
- Manganese minimum 200 mg/day (again, use chelates or polysaccharide trace minerals)

Grape seed extract 3/4 to 1 oz per day (Uckele Health and Nutrition has an
equine product)
B vitamins at twice the level recommended in Chapter Three for two weeks then
at recommended level

*See Chapter Three for guidelines on picking a commercial feed
NOTE: Do not use supplements containing yeast, alfalfa or soybean in any horse
with a history of bloating or any abdominal/digestive problems. Do not use pellet-ed supplements.

CHAPTER SIX

EXERCISE

There is a widespread impression that formal exercise is not appropriate for older horses, it is somehow harmful and the kindest thing we can do is retire the older horse. While the day of mandatory retirement will certainly come for all horses, it is very often done prematurely, when the correct level of exercise in combination with dietary adjustments and physical therapy could have prolonged the horse's useful life by many years. Even when regular use under saddle is no longer possible, some form of formal exercise will still benefit the senior citizen.

The Muscles—Use Them or Lose Them

A very unwelcome consequence of aging is the replacement of muscle mass by fat. This is not just a matter of putting on more fat than

This 20-year-old pony maintains his strength and flexibility with a regular exercise program.

was there at a younger age. The muscles themselves actually get smaller. A swayback, the classical sign of advanced age in horses, is largely caused by loss of muscle and muscular weakness in both the muscles of the back and those of the abdominal wall. The more prominent bony look of many older horses, especially in the hindquarters and over the shoulders, is also largely caused by a lack of muscle bulk.

Exactly why this happens is not entirely clear. Falling levels of the important muscle-stimulating hormones associated with youth certainly plays a role. These include all the sex hormones, growth hormone, thyroid hormone and insulin-like growth factor.

Injections of these hormones in elderly people can actually reverse the signs of aging and return the subjects to a physical condition equivalent to one they had 20 to 30 years previously. New oral supplements are being developed that attempt to achieve the same effect by supplying nutrients that stimulate the pituitary, the body's master gland, to produce more growth hormone. Don't run out to the health food store just yet. How well these supplements work remains to be seen, and the cost for a horse would now run about $700 to $800 a month.

A decreased level of exercise is also definitely involved. Studies have shown that people who exercise regularly and keep it up into

A swayback is the classic sign of advanced age in horses. This condition is largely caused by a lack of muscle.

their later years do not experience that loss of muscle tissue.

Even seniors who go back to exercise after a significant time without a formal program can actually regain much of the lost muscle. Exercise directly effects how much blood flow is going to the muscles and therefore how well they are supplied with the nutrition they need to stay healthy. Especially important is that exercise triggers release of all the hormones important to building muscle mass, in particular growth hormone and insulin-like growth factor. The amount of hormone released in response to exercise does decrease with age, but regular exercise through middle and older age can greatly modify the consequences of that by preventing the muscles from weakening and shrinking in the first place.

The more prominent bony look of many older horses, especially in the hindquarters and over the shoulders, is largely caused by a lack of muscle.

Tendons and Ligaments

The health and strength of tendons and ligaments is directly related to exercise. For one thing, the tone in a tendon is influenced greatly by the tone and strength of the muscle that gives rise to it.

Tendons run from the ends of muscles to bone. Ligaments run from bone to bone. At the bone end, exercise stimulates the cells at the bony attachment to thicken and strengthen. Inside the tendon or ligament itself, the strength/thickness and elasticity/stretch are directly related to how much it is exercised.

As with muscles, and the tissues and organs in the horse's body, there are age-related changes that are inevitable. Many of these will escalate rapidly when formal exercise stops. Turning the horse out into a large field is certainly much better than keeping him in a stall, but it is usually not enough to compensate for lack of a formal exercise program. The horse is just not going to go out there and tell himself he has to keep up a strong working trot for at least 20 to 30 minutes a day to keep his tendons tight.

The Joints

Many horses have their exercise restricted or are retired because of joint problems. Joint degeneration (arthritis) is another one of those age-related problems, caused in part by a lifetime of exercise. However, it is not really exercise that is the culprit but a combination of either extreme exercise or exercise the horse was not conditioned for. Other factors such as poor conformation, improper shoeing and work on hard surfaces and metabolic imbalances in the bone and cartilage caused by inadequate nutrition and age-related slow down of the enzyme and cellular reactions also determine whether cartilage will be repaired or broken down. If you didn't follow all that, don't worry. We'll come back to individual points several times in other chapters. The bottom line here is that exercise is not all that is involved in causing or worsening arthritis.

Exercise is absolutely required to maintain healthy joint cartilage. A joint that is not exercised will show thinning of the cartilage and loss of cushioning power. Joint fluid becomes less viscous/thick and loses lubricating capacity. An excellent example of the importance of exercise is a simple experiment that was done in rabbits with cartilage lesions. They were divided into two groups; one receiving joint injections (equivalent to Adequan™ or hyaluronic acid used in horses) and no exercise; the other the same but with gentle exercise starting almost immediately.

The exercised group had much better cartilage and joint fluid characteristics than the one that was rested. The same thing has been done with injections of corticosteroids, drugs that have largely fallen into disuse because of reports they actually caused damage to the joint cartilage. The steroid experiment clearly showed that injection of steroids had no harmful effects on the cartilage if the joints were rapidly returned to light exercise.

Joint cartilage has no blood vessels supplying it. It must get the nutrients it needs from the joint fluid. Cartilage looks like it's solid

Even at age 30, Jackie, right, never misses a riding lesson and some enjoyable exercise.

but really functions more like a sponge. When the cartilage is compressed during exercise, the fluid sitting inside the cartilage is forced out. When compression lets up (the horse takes the foot off the ground), fresh nutrient-rich joint fluid is taken back up by the cartilage. This pumping action is how the cartilage cells are fed and how they get rid of any harmful waste products or destructive enzymes. The tissue that makes the nourishing joint fluid, the lining (synovial membrane), does have a rich blood supply. Exercise improves blood delivery to the synovial membrane, enhancing removal of harmful wastes or enzymes and ensuring an adequate delivery of nutrition. Joints not exercised regularly are slowly starved into weakness and disease.

Joint health is also influenced by the strength of the muscles, ligaments and other strong connective tissues that hold the bones within the joint into their proper position. Just like muscles and ligaments elsewhere, they will only be toned, strong and flexible if they are regularly used.

Have you ever seen the testimonials on television or in magazines about arthritis spas that worked near miracles for people who were nearly crippled? They have one secret in common—exercise.

Giving children a ride can be good light exercise for an older pony.

The Heart and Lungs

Horses, blessedly, do not have the same types of age-related heart problems as people or even dogs. Part of the reason for this is their diet. Horses do not normally eat large amounts of the harmful fats that contribute to the hardening and eventual clogging of the arteries (see Chapters Three and Four). The fact that many horses are euthanized before they reach an advanced age is also a factor. People are much more likely to invest time and long-term nursing in an elderly relative or house pet than a horse. It is often not physically possible to provide the same level of care to a horse.

However, like any muscle, the horse's heart will lose strength and efficiency if it is not regularly exercised. There are also key enzyme systems related to energy generation within the heart that show decreased activity as a direct effect of age. A combination of supplementation with key nutrients (such as DMG and CoQ10) and formal exercise can go a long way toward preserving strong function of your horse's heart.

Lungs are another matter. Irritants and directly harmful chemicals/pollutants are taking their toll on our horses' lungs as much as our own. Horses with problems like chronic cough, chronic nasal discharge and seasonal sneezing—much like the allergies and asthma people experience—as well as heaves, the equine equivalent of obstructive lung disease and eventually emphysema, are common. Exercise is often a delicate balancing act in these horses but plays an important role in their therapy. Exercise encourages deeper breathing, something we cannot simply instruct the horse to do. It also improves the blood supply to the lungs, making for better uptake of oxygen. It is important to keep as much of the lung open and functioning as possible through exercise to help combat the stiffness that occurs in lungs with aging. Exercise also improves the strength of the abdominal muscles and diaphragm—both used to increase the volume of the chest cavity with exercise. Increased blood flow that occurs along the length of the respiratory tract—from the nose to deep in the lungs—encourages the production of a thin, watery secretion that helps to flush out any impurities or mucus that has accumulated in the lungs.

Turn Out Versus Planned Exercise

Everyone thinks that a turned-out horse will get plenty of exercise. Compared to a horse kept in a small stall, the horse on turn out certainly at least has the potential to get more exercise and probably does cover a wider area in the course of a day. The horse on turn out also can roll or buck freely if the mood strikes him—activities that are important in keeping the spine and its supporting muscles supple and free of kinks or spasms. However, if you count the number of times the horse in the stall and the horse in the pasture actually picked up and put down their feet in the course of a day, there might not be too much difference. And if you are watching to see how often the horse in the field maintained even a walking pace for a length of time significant enough to have any conditioning benefits (at least 20 to 30 minutes without interruption), there are very few who will do this.

How Much Exercise?

Exercising the Older Horse Safely

Before beginning any exercise program with an older horse, make sure his basic diet and supplement program is the best it can be (see Chapters Three, Four and Ten) and he has been on the program for at least a week. It won't do you much good to improve circulation if that blood is not carrying all the nutrients the horse needs to perform the exercise and build strong tissues as a result.

To benefit the horse's general health and the condition of his muscles, ligaments, tendons, joints and cardiopulmonary system, exercise does not have to be hard and heavy. It does have to be suf-

You may want to introduce the older horse to an exercise program by beginning work with the lunge for the first few sessions.

ficiently long and done often enough. Exactly what exercise program is best for any individual horse will depend both on his current level of fitness and any specific health problems he may have. Generally speaking, exercise sufficient to raise the horse's body temperature a few degrees (this is a key trigger to the hormone responses to exercise) and get his heart rate up to about 100 to 140 is enough to benefit the heart and lungs without overstressing the musculoskeletal system. This may correspond to a good working trot for some horses or only a strong walk for a horse that is very out of shape. There is no way to predict this.

You may want to introduce the older horse back to an exercise program by beginning with work on the lunge line for the first few sessions. This is easier for the horse than carrying weight and makes it easier to get those baseline pulse recordings. Keep the horse on a very generous circle and make sure to work the same amount of time in both directions. Most horses are either naturally right or left sided and will go more easily in one direction than the other. Use this time to observe the horse carefully for any areas of stiffness or pain.

The safest way to determine what level of exercise corresponds to these very basic conditioning parameters (temperature and pulse) is to have someone take these measurements for you. Walk the horse for five minutes then immediately take his pulse. This job is made much easier by purchasing an inexpensive stethoscope and listening to the horse's heart rate directly rather than trying to take the pulse at an artery. Simply slide the stethoscope along the lower chest wall

Start an exercise program gradually and be alert for signs of fatigue.

at the level of the elbow, in front of the girth. Move toward the arm pit until you can clearly hear the heart. All but the most severely out-of-condition horses will likely have a pulse well under 100 at this point. To push the pulse higher, pick up a trot or do the same walk on a hill/incline. Once you have found a level of work that gets the horse's pulse in the 120 to 140 range, with a rapid recovery down to a pulse of 90 or below within two minutes, this is the level of exercise you should hold for a week or so. Begin by riding 1/2 to one mile at this rate then recheck the pulse. You want the horse to recover back to a pulse of 90 or under within two minutes. If he does not, shorten the distance until you find a distance he can tolerate within the given ranges for pulse immediately when you stop and pulse at two minutes. Once you have your safe distance for holding the trot determined, follow each trotting interval with a strong walk for twice that distance before trotting again. Continue the alternating trotting and walking for at least 20 minutes, with a goal of 30 minutes. A good goal would be to get the horse to the point he can sustain exercise in the 120 to 140 pulse range for three miles or so before stopping and still be able to recover to a pulse 90 or under within two minutes.

As the horse becomes accustomed to the exercise, you will be able to trot longer distances on the flat or progress to a canter (if the

This 20-year-old quarter horse maintains his strength and flexibility with a regular exercise program.

horse does not have a lameness problem that makes this unwise) or do the same distance on an incline. Before you underestimate the effect that even a slight grade on a hill can have, do it yourself! Cover the same distance on the flat and up a hill. It is important to realize here that the goal is not to get the horse fit to perform; only to introduce enough exercise into his routine to benefit his health. There are no hard and fast rules. If the horse can only tolerate a 1/4-mile trot to begin with, that's fine. With patience and time he will improve, and probably at a much faster rate than you would have anticipated.

Start very slowly, maybe only every other day or twice a week for the first week or two. We all know the stiffness and soreness that can occur the day or two after unaccustomed exercise. The horse may be going through the same thing. Fatigue and soreness lead to changes in gait that may load his legs and muscles in an abnormal way and predispose to injury. We don't want to take any chances here. Remember, any level of sustained exercise is an improvement at this stage.

Warning Signs with Exercise

Be alert to signs of fatigue. Horses that are getting tired will carry their heads lower and may stumble or begin to feel rough gated. Don't hesitate to stop trotting or slow the walk if this occurs. Horses that sweat heavily and out of proportion to the temperature and/or level of exercise may be in pain or do this when fatigue is setting in. If the horse shows heavy breathing or blowing at any stage, slow the work. If pulse recovers much faster than his breathing rate, get a veterinarian to examine the lungs. The level of work we are talking about here would be sufficient to make the horse breathe more deeply and raise his rate a little bit but should not cause him any obvious signs of respiratory distress. Finally, if you hear any irregularities of the heart rate—pauses with no heartbeat heard or a very rapid rate followed by a slow rate then return to rapid, etc.—ask for a veterinary evaluation of that, also. Arrhythmias (abnormal heart rhythms) are more common in older horses.

You will also have to keep a close eye on any areas of previous joint, tendon or ligament injury/disease. This exercise program is very mild and not likely to result in any injury or undue stress. However, joints that have not been worked formally for a long time may experience temporary filling, heat or tenderness. Dealing with this will be covered in detail in Chapter Eight.

CHAPTER SEVEN

ROUTINE
HEALTH CARE

THE BLACKSMITH

I f "No foot, no horse" is true (and it certainly is), then "No good blacksmith, no foot" is also true.

It is estimated between 60% and 80% of all lameness problems originate in the feet, and with good reason. When a horse's feet hurt, he will attempt to land in the most comfortable way possible.

Any landing pattern beyond the normal one dictated by the horse's anatomy will cause uneven distribution of impact shock through all the hoof structures, up the leg, into the shoulder and even into the spine. The horse will also compensate for foot pain up front (or vice versa) by shifting weight onto the hindquarters and/or the opposite good front foot (if he has one). This results very quickly in low back and sacroiliac strain/pain and any number of lameness problems in the joints of the hind end. Many tendon and suspensory injuries are actually caused by the horse trying to shift weight off a leg with a sore foot and ending up overstressing the tendons and ligaments on the previously good side. In fact, by the time the horse is actually examined by a veterinarian he may have so many different problems that the feet get overlooked entirely.

SYMPTOMS OF FOOT PAIN

Standing with legs placed abnormally under the body or abnormally far out in front

Standing with one leg placed further front or further under the body than the other (the sore one)

Abnormally warm feet (check all four and compare front to back on a daily basis)

Exaggerated toe-first or flat-footed landing

Appearance of unusually prominent rings on the foot (not always a sign of founder/laminitis)

Shortened stride in one or both front legs or one or both hind legs

Stiff, choppy gait

More comfortable on grass and in mud than on hard surfaces

Unexplained back pain

Ideally, all horses should be barefoot. Almost any horse, if properly trimmed, can go barefoot.

You should try to find a blacksmith who trims a lot of brood-mares, weanlings and yearlings.

Find out where he goes to trim and inspect the feet of the horses there. The healthy bare foot is typically more upright than the foot of horses who wear shoes, has a relatively short toe and healthy heels and full frogs. The feet do not show signs of chipping, breaking or cracking.

Not all horses are comfortable without shoes. This is usually because a lifetime of wearing them has changed the foot to such a degree that bringing it back to nature would mean a prolonged period of very frequent trimming (there's no such thing as too often, only too much) with the horse probably less than completely comfortable until he can reshape his foot and toughen up the soles. Many people do not want to go to the trouble of doing this and simply keep shoes on their older horses. There are also older horses with degenerative conditions in the feet such as navicular disease or ringbone (see Chapter Ten) that make them more comfortable with special shoes.

If you use shoes, keep them as comfortable and simple as possible. Shoe only the front feet if possible. Shoes called half rounds are perfect for older horses who often have a collection of old injuries or chronic aches and pains that might make them want to move a little differently from day to day to relieve stresses on painful areas that flare up. The half round shoe is flat on the surface that rests against the hoof but rounded on the ground surface. It is a popular shoe for young horses also. With the half round shoe, the horse can change where he breaks over the shoe any way he likes without meeting resistance. These shoes favor easy break over in general and place very little stress on the legs.

Trimming and shoeing or resetting of shoes should be done about every four weeks. Horses with slow growing feet may go a little longer. Horses with problems should never go longer than that.

The exception to every four weeks might be the horse that is barefoot, sound and getting enough exercise to wear his feet naturally.

BEWARE EXTREMES OF TRIMMING

The vogue in recent years is the so-called four point trim, which some may call the natural trim (usually to avoid the bad publicity that goes along with mentioning the four point trim). Seems everyone has heard of this but not too many people really understand the details. The basic premise is that to find out how horses' feet should be trimmed we should look at how horses normally wear their feet in the wild. After studying the feet of mustangs it was noted that they have very short toes compared to domestic/shod horses, very low heels, worn down quarters and most of the weight was being taken on four points—two on either side of the toe and at both heels.

The conclusion was we should drastically change the way we trim domestic horses to match this natural model, and the four point trim was born.

On the surface this makes sense and there are many valid points to the theory. It is certainly true that many domestic horses have toes

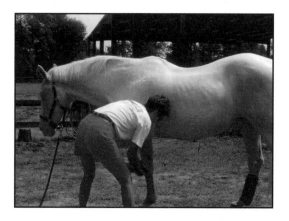

Many health problems may be prevented by paying careful attention to a horse's feet.

that are far too long, which results in forces being directed along an axis that is not ideal. In the natural foot, the pastern and coffin bone line up. The wall of the hoof exactly parallels the coffin bone alignment so that there is not toe extending beyond the point you would predict it to end if you laid two rules side by side, one running with the coffin bone to the ground and one running along the hoof wall. With this conformation to the foot, the weight coming down through the navicular area and the heels is very well cushioned by the internal structures of the foot.

The unshod hoof has a thick digital cushion inside the hoof and healthier deep flexor tendon.

The principle of not allowing too much toe to grow out in front of the horse (edge of toe should be within an inch or so of the tip of the frog) is central to the four point trim but is definitely not a new concept.

The controversial aspects of the four point trim involve cutting back the heels and taking weight off the quarters. It is assumed that, because these structures are worn down very short in wild horses, it is a good thing. However, that's not necessarily the case. You also have to consider the type of terrain the wild horses were covering. Dry, rock-hard ground surface will cause more natural wear than soft ground or pastures. Horses with their toes at a correct length can still be in normal alignment and wear with more heel and weight bearing all around the foot.

The biggest black eye for the four point trim has been the reports of horses going extremely lame afterward. This is caused as much by making drastic changes to the foot all at one time as it is by the type of changes made. If you are going to make changes in the shape of the horse's foot, do so gradually to allow the bones, tendons and soft tissues time to adjust to the new stresses. It never makes sense to make a change so severe that the horse is lame as a result.

THE DENTIST

The earlier chapters on diet stressed the importance of regular dental care, especially for older horses. High-quality grains and hays will not do the horse any good if they cannot be digested and the first step in that is to have them thoroughly chewed. Chewing cracks the hard coatings on grains, exposing the nutritious interior to digestive enzymes. It physically weakens the structure of tough plant materials and breaks them into smaller pieces so that there is more surface area exposed to digestion. The flow of saliva is stimulated by chewing. Saliva itself contains digestive enzymes and other substances to aid digestion.

Finding a competent equine dentist is no small feat in many areas. Blacksmiths and other lay people sometimes make a little money on the side by floating teeth but rarely do a good enough job for an older horse's needs and definitely are not qualified to handle any of the more complicated dental problems an older horse may have. The only solution is to persevere until you locate a good dentist in the area or one that is willing to travel to your location. It may help to have several other people lined up to have their horses' teeth done, too, and to arrange for all horses to be in one location or a limited number of barns located in close proximity to each other. There is no veterinary dental association, so you will have to start by calling all the local vets in the phone book. If this does not yield anyone willing to do teeth, call the closest large equine clinic or hospital. If necessary, ship your horse to the dentist. It is well worth the effort.

Older horses should have their teeth floated and mouths thoroughly examined every six months. In between visits, be alert to the signs of an oral problem, which include:

• dropping grain or hay while chewing

• hay wadding up inside the mouth while chewing

- a new habit of dipping hay in water while eating or dropping a lot of grain into the water
- loss of appetite for dry feeds
- weight loss without loss of appetite
- unusual (bad) odor to the breath

VACCINATIONS

Vaccinations are not harmless, are not 100% effective and should always be considered a stress to the horse. However, the benefits of certain vaccines far outweigh any dangers. The need for each type of vaccination should be carefully weighed and matched to your individual circumstances.

With older horses, it is best to time any vaccinations (except emergency tetanus) for a time when the horse is healthy, vigorous and not going to be stressed in any way for the two weeks prior to and after the vaccination. Spring is usually the ideal time; vaccinating after the good grass has come in but before biting insects have become a big problem.

Rhinopneumonitis and Influenza: These are both viral respiratory diseases. Rhino vaccines are notoriously short-lived with maximum protection lasting only about 2 months. As the horse ages, his susceptibility to rhinopneumonitis lessens until he reaches a very advanced age when the likelihood of picking up this, or any other, infection will again likely begin to rise. I do not routinely recommend rhino vaccines for older horses unless they are kept in barns or turn out conditions where their likelihood of exposure is very high. The horses at highest risk of bringing in this infection are those that race or show frequently, young stock coming in from multiple different locations and broodmares who ship out to breed.

Influenza infections are usually more serious (make the horse more ill) than rhinopneumonitis. Horses will have antibodies against strains of flu they have encountered over the past few years but new strains are constantly arising. Unfortunately, vaccine reactions are also more likely and severe with flu. Local abscesses or sterile swellings, fever, loss of appetite and depression are all fairly common with flu vaccines, especially in older horses. I personally prefer an approach that boosts their natural immunity with daily feeding of vitamin C and bioflavinoids, combined with protecting the older horse from exposure to new or sick horses or any areas where those horses have been stabled or turned out. However, if you cannot very strictly adhere to those rules, or if your horse will unavoidably be at high risk of exposure, the vaccine reaction risk may be far preferable to having the horse get very ill from a full-blown infection. You should discuss your individual situation carefully with your veterinarian.

Tetanus: Tetanus recommendations are easy. Every horse needs tetanus vaccination. Horses are among the most susceptible animals to tetanus and it is everywhere in their environment. Tetanus vaccinations are historically given on a yearly basis (although no one really knows if they are needed that often) and rarely have serious side effects.

Strangles: Strangles vaccines, except for the new intranasal variety, have the highest incidence of unpleasant and serious side effects. Once exposed to Strangles, horses will develop a lifelong immunity and do not need vaccinations. There are a few exceptions to this, but the chance of a vaccine making those horses any more resistant is extremely small. If their immune system did not respond normally to a natural infection, it is not going to react any better to a vaccine—at least not an injectable vaccine. The new intranasal Strangles vaccines only provide boosted immunity along the nasal passages—the usual route of entry of the Strangles bacterium. However, side effects are rare and mild with this approach. If you and your veterinarian decide Strangles vaccine is in order for your horse under your particular circumstances, consider using only the intranasal form of the vaccine.

Encephalitis: Equine encephalitis is another viral disease that may strike horses in three forms—Eastern, Western or Venezuelan. The latter is rarely found in the U.S. except for areas close to the Mexican border. This disease can also make people ill. It is spread by biting insects, not by contact with a sick animal. Despite good vaccines, the disease is still prevalent in many areas of this country—at least in part because of failure of people to vaccinate their horses. Everyone should do their part to bring this devastating disease under control by making sure their horse is vaccinated every year—twice a year in the southern states where insects remain a problem year round. Side effects are usually mild and may go unnoticed. Many people find it convenient to combine tetanus vaccination with encephalitis vaccination every year—getting the two big must-have vaccines taken care of at the same time.

Rabies: Unfortunately, because of the reservoir of the rabies virus in wild animal populations, horses are at risk. Horses with rabies are more difficult to recognize than dogs or wild animals with the disease. The horse does not become violent or try to bite you, but it does become subdued, depressed and weak, eventually showing signs of staggering and incoordination that signal a disease of the brain and nervous system. Rabies can be mistaken for many things, i.e., poisoning, EPM and encephalitis. By the time they are actually diagnosed as having a nervous system disease, there is a very real danger the virus could be spread to anyone who works around the horse's mouth. For your horse's protection and your own, rabies vaccination should be done every year. Be prepared for possible vaccine reactions, especially high fever and a few days' loss of appetite. Do not vaccinate for rabies within two weeks of any other vaccine, a deworming or any other form of stress such as unusual exercise or shipping. Symptoms can be controlled with bute (phenylbutazone) if necessary without interfering with the vaccine's effect on the immune system.

Botulism and Potomac Horse Fever: I group these two vaccines together because they are both only strongly indicated for horses in specific geographical areas. Botulism can occur at any time and in any place. It may even be related to a freak accident such as the outbreak in California where the organism found its way into a supply of hay after rabbits were caught up in baling equipment and baled with hay—botulism from their intestinal tracts contaminated the hay. However, there are certain areas of the country, sometimes limited to a single county, where botulism tends to occur with greater frequency and for reasons that are not well understood. Because it is a relatively rare disease, many owners of older horses elect not to subject their animals to the stress of this vaccine, which requires a series of injections. Again, if you have any doubts or questions, by all means discuss them with your veterinarian. In general though, this should not be on the routine vaccination list.

Potomac Horse Fever is a relatively new disease of horses (newly recognized at least) that causes initial fever and depression, colic commonly associated with diarrhea and founder/laminitis. An estimated 5% to 30% of untreated cases will die. It is concentrated in areas close to major rivers, primarily from the Mississippi eastward, and peak number of cases are seen in the hottest months of the year. There are also particular states and areas within states where the incidence is higher. PHF vaccine is effective, and natural exposure to the organism also results in the horse developing antibodies. Whether or not you need to vaccinate depends on where you are located. The best approach is to contact both your veterinarian and your state agricultural extension agent for information on how often the disease strikes horses in your area.

WEST NILE ENCEPHALITIS

1999 saw the emergence of a new viral encephalitis—West Nile encephalitis. Like Eastern, Western and Venezuelan, this disease is caused by a virus. There are many other similarities with the other types of encephalitis. This one, too, can infect people (although the disease is less serious in people, causing only about 10% mortality compared to 40% to 50% in horses). It is also transmitted by mosquitoes and possibly other blood-sucking insects such as ticks. The reservoir of the disease (species that harbor the virus without it killing them and keep the cycle alive) is probably wild birds,⟶

and the virus has been detected in many different species of birds since the outbreak. The disease appeared in a cluster of horses on Long Island late in the summer of 1999. At the end of the mosquito season in the Northeast, no horse cases had been found outside this group, but the entire Eastern seaboard may be at risk next year, and migrating birds could carry the virus farther south (it has already been found as far south as Maryland).

Because this is a new virus on this continent, horses will have absolutely no natural immunity, and the vaccines for the other types of encephalitis will be totally ineffective against this strain (no cross protection from the vaccines). There are no approved or even experimental vaccines available at the time of this printing. The Japanese do have a modified live virus experimental vaccine (virus alive but modified so that it doesn't cause disease when injected), but most experts feel this is too risky to use because of the chance the virus could change back into a disease-producing form.

Until a vaccine becomes available, measures to protect your horse should include:

- Maintenance of a strong immune system through sound basic nutrition and possibly immune-stimulating supplements
- Wise planning of needed vaccines well before mosquito season so that the horse's immune system is not stressed at that time
- Liberal use of insect repellent
- Keep horses inside, in screened stalls, at peak mosquito times, which are dusk, dawn and the night hours

DEWORMING

The last important aspect of routine health care is deworming. Much has changed in the way we deworm our horses over last 15 to 20 years—all for the better. Gone are the days of chemicals so toxic the horse needed to be fasted first. Gone is the necessity to pass a stomach tube to deworm the horse. We now have a variety of very effective paste wormers that owners can safely and effectively use themselves, without the need of a veterinarian. However, with this convenience comes a responsibility to understand what is going on with the parasites that can affect horses and not be taken in by all the high-pressure advertising from drug companies.

People may not think of dewormers as drugs, but a certain amount of the medication will be absorbed and must be broken down by the horse's liver. As with vaccinations, deworming should be considered a necessary evil and a stress to the horse's system. Do not time vaccinations and dewormings within two weeks of each other. Do not deworm horses who have received any other medica-

Much has changed in the way we deworm horses over the last 15 to 20 years—and all for the better, say veterinarians and horse owners.

People may not think of dewormers as drugs, but a certain amount of medication will be absorbed and must be metabolized by the liver.

tion—prescription or not—within two weeks of the deworming. Do not deworm an ill horse, a horse who has coliced recently or a horse that is under, or going to be under, any unusual stress. Horses in poor condition should be dewormed very cautiously and usually should have the benefit of veterinary input in the choice of the dewormer and any other treatment the horse may need first or at the same time to prevent side effects. You won't find these precautions prominently printed on the box of your dewormer, but they are important, especially for older horses with more sensitive systems. You should also know that many dewormers, especially the newer ones like ivermectin and moxidectin, can be toxic to pets. Clean up any spills and dispose of containers properly.

The vast majority of horses of any age will handle their encounter with deworming drugs without any problems. The alternative of not deworming the horse is certainly putting him at a much higher risk of health problems than using dewormers. The advent of paste dewormers has done much to reduce and even virtually eliminate some types of parasite-related colic and other health problems. By all means deworm your horse. Just be aware you are using a drug and should time the treatment accordingly.

Different owners, even different vets, deworm on different schedules. There is not necessarily any one right or wrong way to do

Dewormers, especially the newer ones such as ivermectin, can be toxic to pets. Clean up any spills and dispose of containers properly.

it, although there are rules that should be followed, and an understanding of the parasites helps immensely.

Intestinal parasites and immature forms of parasites that can cause skin conditions like open, weeping areas on the belly of the horse are more active and more of a problem during the spring, summer and early fall. There is even evidence to suggest that some parasites may enter a dormant stage in the late fall and winter, only to emerge from your horse's tissues as spring weather arrives. It makes sense therefore to be especially vigilant about deworming during those times.

Parasite Types

Large Strongyles (bloodworms) used to be the most dangerous parasite in horses—damaging both the intestines and the blood supply to the intestines and other areas. However, regular worming, especially with ivermectin and some other drugs that can kill at least some of the immature forms (like fenbendazole) has virtually eliminated this threat to your horse's health. The small strongyles are taking over as your horse's most important parasite.

All paste wormers on the market today are effective against adult small strongyles. If your horse, and the horses he is exposed to, have been on regular frequent wormings, small strongyles will not be a problem. Ivermectin kills some of the immature life stages of small strongyles, increasing the horse's protection. However, only the new dewormer, moxidectin, is effective in killing life stages that have invaded the wall of the intestine and become dormant. The dormant forms are picked up over the course of warm seasons and will wait out the winter only to emerge in large numbers when spring rolls around. Moxidectin given in late February or early March (or whatever time corresponds to just before spring in your area) will kill these dormant forms before they have a chance to emerge and cause problems such as colic or diarrhea. Moxidectin costs more than other wormers, often twice as much, but is worth the investment at least at this time of year.

Bots—large parasites that dig holes in the lining of the stomach—are a special case. Ivermectin is definitely the drug of choice for these nasty bugs; give once in late summer and again in early winter. Moxidectin probably also has activity against bots, but there was insufficient data of its effectiveness to satisfy the FDA so it is not currently recommended for bot removal.

There are various other parasites that will compete for your horse's food, irritate or damage his intestines, interfere with digestion, place a constant stress on his immune system and predispose him to other diseases that enter the horse through damaged intestines. All of these can be effectively treated by either ivermectin or moxidectin.

Timing of Deworming

Horses kept in stalls and sharing paddocks with other horses on a rotating basis or horses on turnout with less than or equal to one to two acres/horse need intensive deworming. Every four weeks is best, especially for older horses. You can use ivermectin every time with a once-a-year moxidectin treatment; moxidectin every time with twice-a-year deworming for bots using ivermectin; or rotate these two with other classes of dewormers over the year.

For horses under less crowded conditions, deworming every four to six weeks during the warm months of the year is a good precaution, although you may be able to get away with every eight weeks. Best approach is to have a few fecal examinations done just before your next scheduled eight-week interval deworming to make sure egg counts are not too high before deciding on an every-eight-weeks approach. With every eight-week worming, use ivermectin and moxidectin at the specific times described above and during peak parasite season (spring, early summer). After that, you can rotate the other dewormers without sacrificing effectiveness.

Another option under the less crowded conditions is use of a daily dewormer, Strongid C. Plan to begin the program during the winter, when parasite numbers are at their lowest. Treat the horse first with a dose of moxidectin to remove encysted small strongyles, then after three weeks with ivermectin to remove any other remaining parasites. The daily worming program is only effective if you are religious about making sure the daily dose gets into the horse every day. It is not suitable for field feeding conditions where stronger horses may get more than their equal share of feed (and dewormer).

Types of Deworming Drugs

Ivermectin (Zimecterin, Eqvalan, Rotectin I and Equimectrin) and moxidectin (Quest) are the two superstars of deworming drugs, controlling a wider range of parasites and more different life stages than other classes of dewormers. Ivermectin's list of controlled species and life stages exceeds moxidectin's. Extensive use of ivermectin is probably responsible for saving more horses from parasite-related colic and blood vessel damage than any other preventative medicine measure in recent memory. The drug is so effective, it is believed to be responsible for the emergence of new clinical problems associated with parasites and life stages that it does not kill—namely tapeworm infestations and problems with encysted (dormant) stages of small strongyles. Moxidectin's greatest claim to fame is that it is effective against encysted forms of small strongyles. Its greatest drawback is that it is not effective against the immature life stage of roundworms that migrate extensively in foals and is also not effective against the life stage of threadworms that is transmitted to foals via their mother's milk. The drug is also not cleared for bots by the FDA, although more extensive studies in other countries suggest it may be almost as effective against bots. Like ivermectin, it is not effective against tapeworms.

Pyrimidine wormers (pyrantels—Strongid P, Strongid T, Rotectin II and Strongid C) are a separate class of deworming drug that is extremely safe and highly palatable, making it possible to deworm the horse by adding the liquid to the feed. There is also a pelleted form administered on a daily basis for constant control (but not elimination) of worm burdens. Among pyrantel's advantages is that it can be used in double doses (Strongid or Rotectin II) to treat for tapeworms. (This is an extra label use, not officially recommended or endorsed, but commonly used by veterinarians. Consult yours first before doing this.)

The benzimadazoles, notably thiabendazole (Equizole), fenbendazole (Panacur) and oxibendazole (Anthelcide EQ), are another very broad spectrum and effective class of wormers but the ones most likely to be associated with resistance problems. Closely related, and with similar range of effectiveness, are the probenzimadazoles oxfendazole (Benzelmin, EQUI-CIDE) and febantel. All are 95%+ effective against adult large and small strongyles, pinworms and roundworms. Oxibendazole at 1.5 times the usual dose will kill threadworms. Parasites have the potential to become resistant to not only any given member of the class but also partially or equally resistant to other members of the class. This is called cross resistance. One member, fenbendazole (Panacur or Safeguard) can be used like ivermectin or moxidectin to kill the dangerous immature forms of the large strongyle (bloodworm). Double doses are used for this purpose, for four or five days straight. This program is often recommended on large farms to treat incoming animals and make sure they are not going to start contaminating the premises with parasites shortly after their arrival. This is sometimes termed purge worming as the intensive treatment is designed to kill as many parasites as possible.

Piperazine (Alfalfa pellet) is a narrow spectrum but very safe drug, primarily of use in rotational worming programs for foals. It has good results against roundworms and small strongyles but is only 80% effective with pinworms and less than 50% effective against the dangerous large strongyles.

Dichlorvos is an organo-phosphate (yes, same as the insecticides!) which used to be the mainstay of treatment for bots. However, it had a very narrow safety range and even within this range could cause side effects. Use of dichlorvos also required withholding food and water for several hours before and after treatment. The arrival of ivermectin on the deworming scene has made dichlorvos obsolete.

You may soon see the arrival of yet another new dewormer—Doramectin. This drug has activity that is very similar to moxidectin's and has already been approved for use in cattle. It may become available in a convenient new and effective form—injection.

Note: I sometimes hear of people treating their horses with injectable ivermectin. This is a drug designed and cleared only for cattle that can have fatal complications if injected into horses. There is currently no approved form of injectable dewormer for horses. Never give permission for your horse to have an injectable wormer. If Doramectin is eventually approved for injection into horses, you can be sure the packaging will very clearly state that it is approved for horses. If you don't see that, don't use it.

CHAPTER EIGHT

THE SCOURGE OF ARTHRITIS

What Is Arthritis?

In the very simplest terms, arthritis is degeneration of a joint. Arthritis may involve thinning and loss of the slippery joint cartilage at the ends of the bones, inflammation and thickening of the lining of the joints (synovitis), build up of new bone at irritated edges of a joint (osteophytes), and thickening, weakening or tears of the tissue surrounding the joint (the joint capsule). Any of these changes can be found with arthritis.

Arthritis in people is generally of two distinct types—degenera-

This is Sonny, a 20-year-old quarter horse owned by the Thomases of Harrodsburg, Kentucky. Sonny is described by his owners as having "done it all" from novice eventing to trail riding, circus tricks, giving lessons and is equally at home in English or Western gear. Sonny has short upright pasterns and an upright foot. Over the years he has developed a choppy, stilted gait related to arthritic changes in his feet (probable ringbone with potential contribution from navicular disease). Joint nutraceuticals were not helpful, but Sonny had a very dramatic response to treatment with magnetic bell boots. He wears them up to 20 hours a day and shows a much freer and pain-free gait when working as a result.

tive or osteoarthritis and rheumatoid arthritis. Rheumatoid arthritis is a condition where the body develops antibodies that attack its own joint tissues. There is usually more inflammation and heat involved with rheumatoid arthritis. Cause is unknown and there is no cure. Rheumatoid arthritis is said not to exist in horses—at least no one has confirmed it does as yet.

Osteoarthritis is the type found in horses. Like older people, most older horses have osteoarthritis in one or more joints. It is an almost inevitable age-associated change. A history of speed sports, sharp turns, pounding on hard surfaces, joint injuries, joint infections complicated by improper shoeing and/or conformation faults all make arthritis more likely, more severe and more likely to appear earlier. There are also some changes in body chemistry caused by aging that predispose to arthritis.

With all the multiple insults and injuries that a horse's joints

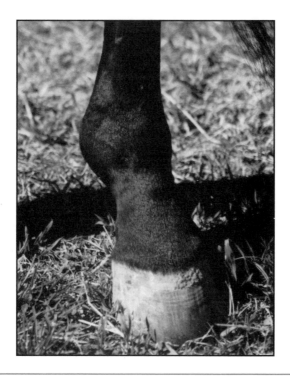

Recent research suggests it's possible to minimize and even reverse the damage caused by arthritis. This horse has a visibly arthritic ankle.

must bear during his life, and considering the sheer weight of the horse, it would seem that arthritis is indeed inevitable and something the horse will just have to learn to live with. However, recent arthritis research in both animals and humans has shown that correcting the biochemical, age-related defects in joint metabolism can make all the difference between an animal that is crippled or at least severely limited by arthritis and one that continues to exercise comfortably well into advanced age. There is evidence that it is possible to repair and reverse many of the changes of arthritis.

BUILDING A THERAPY PROGRAM

Exercise

The key to a successful arthritis therapy program is to first remove any changeable physical causes. This does not mean to stop exercising the horse. Without regular exercise, joint cartilage is not properly nourished and becomes thinner, more easily damaged. The joint capsule also may become thickened and stiff; tendons shortened and less flexible. In time, these changes become permanent or at least so painful to work through that your chances of reversing them are very slim. Lack of exercise will contribute to arthritis, not help it.

Obviously the advice to keep exercising has to be tempered with some common sense. A joint that is hot, swollen, tender and making the horse obviously lame is inflamed and needs a short period of rest until it can cool/calm down. Many people use anti-inflammatory drugs like phenylbutazone to treat acutely inflamed joints. However, nothing works better than ice. Application of ice, done as quickly as possible and for as long a period of time as possible until the joint is cooled out, is by far the safest and most effective treatment. Phenylbutazone (bute) interferes with joint cartilage metabolism and has quite a few other undesirable side effects like damage to the protective lining of the intestines, resulting in ulcers, and kidney damage. Older horses are especially prone to side effects of all types of drugs and bute is no exception. You can get better effects in a shorter period of time just by keeping the joint wrapped in ice. Gentle, sane exercise such as walking should begin as soon as the joint has cooled out, with liberal use of ice after any type of exercise to avoid relapses.

The type of exercise is also important. Again, common sense

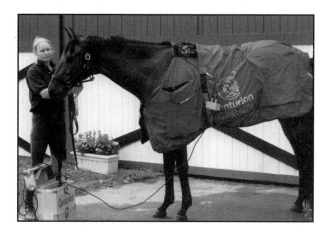

This horse wears a magnetic therapy blanket. Magnetic therapy uses magnets or copper wires to generate a magnetic field. This treatment is said to relieve pain and stiffness.

must prevail. A horse that is very stiff from old arthritis or lame from an arthritis flare up may not tolerate much more than walking.

Sustained walking for 20 to 30 minutes once or twice a day will work wonders in making the horse more comfortable. Any signs of inflammation may be controlled with ice. You can also ease aching and make the horse more comfortable before exercise by use of heat. Heat gel packs or towels soaked in hot water and refreshed every 20 minutes work well. Use of liniments and bandaging with cotton or use of Neoprene joint wraps are excellent ways to warm stiff and sore joints. Once again, the results you get will be much better than with anti-inflammatory or pain relieving drugs and will last far longer, too. All it takes is your commitment to invest a little time into making the horse as comfortable as possible.

Walking and trotting are the cornerstones of the exercise program for arthritis. Gentle cantering can be added as the horse becomes more comfortable. Occasional jumping may even be okay.

How much the horse will eventually be able to do is a very individual thing—depending on the horse's desire and the nature of his arthritis, not to mention how devoted you are to controlling and reversing it. The most important thing to remember is to keep the horse moving, a minimum of 30 minutes per day sustained work at a comfortable pace. It may take weeks of careful exercise for an older horse that has been out of work for a long time to regain flexibility and work through the aches and pains of resuming exercise. If you persevere the results will be well worth it.

Correcting External Causes

It doesn't make much sense to institute an arthritis program if some of the causes of the problem are left uncorrected. Extreme exercise such as speed work, jumping, sharp turns and high-level dressage movements will have to be stopped in favor of slower more relaxed work until the problem is controlled.

A detailed and critical inspection of the feet is in order. Is the horse wearing his shoes normally and equally on both sides. Does the wear at the toe occur right at the center of the foot? Are the heels the same length? Uneven wear can indicate a horse that is moving abnormally in attempts to put less weight on a painful area. However, if the uneven wear is due to uneven trimming, you are likely contributing to the arthritis. Both blacksmith and vet should be involved in this evaluation. Do not hesitate to change to a shoe that will ease the horse's way of going (rolled toe or half round shoe) or even to leave the horse barefoot and properly trimmed for a few weeks. If in doubt, definitely choose one of these three options— they don't lock the horse into any particular way of going.

You cannot do much of anything to change conformation faults. What you can do is make sure that the rest of the horse's leg is lined up to properly absorb the shock of movement. The horse may paddle or wing his feet but what really matters is how the bones are lined up when the foot hits the ground. For example, a horse with an offset cannon bone or pastern—bones do not sit squarely under the knee—will normally move his foot in an arc to either the inside or outside, but the foot will land flat. Owners sometimes complain the horse does not move straight and their blacksmiths will intentionally lower one side or the other of the hoof to change how the horse moves. This looks better but places tremendous strains on the joints. My personal preference for hoof care for a horse starting an arthritis program is to leave the shoes off unless the horse has a painful foot condition like a corn or sole bruising that requires shoes (an exception may be the horse with ringbone or navicular disease, which will be discussed separately). Trim the toe back somewhat—with the ultimate goal of having the edge of the toe about one inch from the point of the frog but knowing you cannot take off this much toe in one trimming. Round off the toe. Any outside flares should be smoothed out as much as possible without taking off too much hoof wall. Leave most or all of the sole intact—no heavy paring out, and same for the heels. The goal is to make the horse move comfortably and in whatever way makes him most comfortable. Almost all horses will be obviously more comfortable without their shoes.

Reversing Old-Age Biochemistry

I was skeptical about joint supplements when they first hit the market. How could a teaspoonful of ground-up cow cartilage make a horse build strong joints? I was wrong. Joint nutraceuticals (nutritional substances with medical activity) are to arthritis what ivermectin was to worming. They are changing our entire approach to arthritis—for the better.

Research has shown that aging is associated with an imbalance between the processes that build and repair cartilage and those that break it down. These changes can be reversed by providing the horse with an external source of the nutrients he uses to build cartilage. These work by both stimulating the cells to take those nutrients in and make cartilage and by blocking or tying-up the enzymes that are destroying them. In essence, you flood the joints with what they need to build cartilage and inactivate destructive processes at the same time so that the balance is tipped back in favor of repairing the cartilage.

Glucosamine

Glucosamine is a simple substance, a combination of sugar (glucose) and a protein (the amine part). Amino sugars form the backbone of all the important joint (and tendon/ligament) substances, like chondroitin sulfate. Because it is such a basic chemical, it can be used in whatever way the body needs it. Its simplicity also means it is absorbed very well from the intestinal tract. In my experience, glucosamine is the fastest acting and most reliable of the joint supplements. Results are very often seen in less than a week—often dramatic results. Long-term use of this supplement will also help reverse the cartilage damage of arthritis. I prefer the glucosamine HCl form to glucosamine sulfate because some horses do not like the slight odor of the glucosamine sulfate, and it seems to work just as well. You get what you pay for with these supplements. Glucosamine is less expensive than chondroitins but will still cost you close to $1 a day, at least to start, for some products. Bargain brands are no bargain since you sacrifice quality.

Begin treatment at 10 grams per day of glucosamine. I suggest continuing this for at least one month. You can then try gradually dropping the dose down to a low of five grams per day. If the horse's comfort level worsens at any time, go back to the higher dose and, if necessary, stay there.

Chondroitin Sulfate

Chondroitin sulfate is only one of several important joint cartilage substances but is present in very large amounts in joint cartilage. Unlike glucosamine, chondroitin is a very large and complicated molecule with a structure like a wire bottle cleaning brush. There is no doubt that chondroitin has a powerful effect on joint carti- lage. It both stimulates the production of cartilage and blocks the activity of cartilage-destroying enzymes. The problem is that it is very poorly absorbed in the intestine. Probably only about 10% of the chondroitin you give orally actually makes it to the joint in that form. The rest is digested to some extent before absorption or not absorbed at all.

Chondroition products are available as pure chondroitin sulfate (which is really somewhere between 80% and 95% chondroitin, depending on the assay used to test for it) or mixed chondroitin sul- fates that contain chondroitins other than the joint-specific one.

There are also products called mixed mucopolysaccharides or mixed glycosaminoglycans. These last two and the mixed chondroitins are the same thing. They are the dehydrated ground cartilage (usually tracheas from cows) that are used as sources of chondroitin. The pure ones have had the chondroitin concentrated out and are more expensive.

In my experience, the mixed products often work just as well as pure chondroitins at a much lower cost. However, none of them work as rapidly or predictably as glucosamine. One exception to this rule is a recently marketed liquid mucopolysaccharide-based product called CortaFlx that pretreats the raw cartilage base to make it more absorbable. This particular product works very well. Manufacturers are constantly developing new ways to process and deliver joint nutraceuticals. Look for more liquid joint supplements to hit the store shelves soon. To be comparable to glucosamine and CortaFlx, they will have to show you dramatic improvements in five days or so. If you don't see this you should switch to the other type of supplements and/or make sure what you are trying to treat is really an arthritis condition that will respond.

Initial effect dose for chondroitins (pure or mixed) is 7,500 mg per day unless you use CortaFlx liquid. This dose should be continued for at least a month before trying to drop it back to about 5,000 mg a day. In my experience, dosages lower than this will not get good results.

You will also find joint products that contain shark cartilage. Shark cartilage has been shown to be of benefit in the treatment of arthritis, just like cartilage taken from cows, but does not seem to work any better than the other cartilage sources and costs much more. There is also the distinct disadvantage that a horse may dislike the smell and taste of it. Until it can be processed to get rid of that odor/taste and until studies have proven it is superior to bovine cartilage, I would avoid it.

Perna Mussel

Perna is a mussel—a marine creature that has a cartilage skeleton instead of bone. Some joint supplements use dehydrated perna as the base, sometimes mixed with chondroitin or glucosamine. In addition to the joint substances, perna provides a wealth of minerals and amino acids, the function of which we do not understand very well. Perna alone takes longer to work, often up to two to three weeks. However, results are often excellent, especially in older horses. The effects also last longer (a month or more) if you stop the supplement. Combinations of perna and glucosamine seem to work especially well in older horses.

The initial dosage is the same as for chondroitins. If using a product that also contains glucosamine, make sure there is enough in there that the horse gets a minimum of five grams per day.

Other Nutritional Supports

There are several other nutrients that play a key role in joint health. Some supplements will contain either chondroitins, glucosamine or Perna plus one or more of these key supplements.

Manganese is a mineral needed for joint health and normal formation of cartilage. An effective supplementary dose would be a minimum of 100 mg/day.

Copper is also needed for the health of all connective tissues. Minimum supplementary dose for most diets would be 50 mg/day. Vitamin C and the related substances, bioflavinoids, are important antioxidants that combat cell damage. It is best to provide your vitamin C and antioxidant supplements separately rather than as part of a mixture. Horses on plenty of fresh grass will not need these, but those on hay rations do. Make sure the horse gets at least 4.5 grams of vitamin C per day and 25 to 50 grams of bioflavinoids.

Sulfur is very important to the formation of joint cartilage. The horse naturally gets his sulfur from the sulfur-containing amino acids, but these may be in short supply in some diets.

I prefer supplementation with methionine, one to two grams per day, to boost the horse's sulfur intake.

Pure methionine supplements are hard to find. There are a limited number of amino acid supplements that will contain just lysine (the most important amino acid) and methionine, usually with vitamin B6—the vitamin most important to processing protein. It may be easier to find methionine supplements designed for horses with bad feet. These will also contain the vitamin biotin and the mineral zinc. Choose one that has zinc in the same level as your manganese supplement. This will balance the trace minerals. Some people use the supplement MSM, methylsulfonylmethane, as a nutritional source of sulfur. This is far more economical and works for many horses. It is fed at about 10 grams per day and is very economical if you shop around, being available for as little as 40¢ a day. MSM is protected by a patent, which means it comes from a single source and price differences only amount to bigger profits for the company that is packaging it and putting their label on it.

A few raw/unprocessed vegetable oils contain high amounts of essential fatty acids. These substances prompt the body to manufacture chemicals and chemical messengers that, among other things, assist in the control of inflammation. Essential fatty acid supplementation is an important aspect of nutrition to consider for the older horse since age is associated with decreased ability of the body to carry out some of the steps in manufacturing these chemicals. The essential fatty acid supplements jump start this process. Flaxseed is the best source. The unprocessed oil (processed oils, like those you buy in grocery stores, have the fatty acids destroyed) can be purchased at health food stores. They must be refrigerated to maintain their potency. Cold-processed flaxseed meal is also available (Missing Link™, Designing Health). Horses love it. In addition to helping with the pain and stiffness of arthritis, your horse's coat will look better than ever.

SUGGESTED SUPPLEMENT PROGRAM FOR ARTHRITIS

Glucosamine 10 grams per day
And/or
Chondroitin or perna-based supplement 7.5 grams per day
Manganese minimum 100 mg/day
Copper minimum 50 mg/day
Zinc (to balance manganese and copper) minimum 150 mg/day
Vitamin C minimum 4.5 grams per day
Bioflavinoids minimum 25 grams/day
Methionine minimum 1 to 2 grams/day
Or
MSM 10 grams per day
Flaxseed oil 6 tbsp or flaxseed meal, cold processed, 1/2 cup per day

Laser therapy uses light waves to treat pain.

OLD FASHIONED PHYSICAL THERAPY

Hot and Cold

Investing the time in providing heat or cold therapy may get better results without the side effects and cost of using medications in almost all circumstances. Heat works best on old injuries that cause stiffness and pain. You can recognize the benefits because the horse gets better as he works rather than worse. Warm wet towels placed under a layer of plastic will provide heat for anywhere from 30 to 60 minutes or longer, depending on the initial temperature. Massage, especially massage with a light liniment such as Absorbine or the mouthwash Listerine also creates heat, as does simply bandaging the area. A special treat for sore feet and legs is the use of a warm poultice, which heats very easily in a microwave. A quick and mess-free method is to put the amount you need in a plastic sandwich bag (packing feet) or food storage bag (legs/joints). Seal the bag, heat in the microwave. To apply, make sure the poultice is not too hot, then cut down the seams of the bag to form an outside plastic wrap of the size and shape you need. Place the poultice with outside plastic onto the foot or leg, mold and secure with an outside wrap.

Cold as ice or cold water is indicated for old injuries that flare up, old injuries immediately after a hard work (followed by heat) and for all new joint problems. Keep using cold until the joint stays cool an hour after the last cold application. You can buy cold wraps for horses that use either cold water, gel packs or ice inserts, but not all work well.

Make sure you get one with a guarantee so you can get your money back if they heat up too quickly. Another approach that eliminates the guess work and chance of trying different products is simply to pack sandwich or food storage bags with crushed ice (pea size chunks work best). I keep several of these in the freezer at all times. Cotton wraps soaked in alcohol can also be kept in the freezer and will not freeze. These provide an easy way to get quick cooling to a leg. You can also deep cool your poultice by putting it in the freezer (use the same plastic bag method as above) for at least an hour.

New Therapeutic Approaches

Everyone is interested in finding a treatment for arthritis pain that does not involve the long-term administration of pain-killing medications; something that is both safe and possibly even beneficial to use. These alternative therapies come and go with variations on old themes popping up all the time. Some are legitimate and helpful, others are a hoax.

Magnetic Therapy

There is growing interest in magnetic therapy for arthritis and a growing body of scientific literature that supports it. To say we don't know how it works is an understatement. Scientists are unable to agree on even the effects it has on the body let alone how it might create those effects.

Magnetic therapy is of two basic types—static or permanent magnets and electromagnetic field therapy. In the first, the magnets are similar to those common in everyday use. With the electromagnetic therapy, an electrical current is passed through copper wires and generates a magnetic field. The magnetic field from the electromagnetic devices penetrates much deeper than the static or permanent magnets.

The most obvious benefit from magnetic therapy of either type, in horses that respond, is relief of pain and stiffness. Some horses respond very dramatically to magnetic therapy, others little if at all. Some of the failures could be due to misdiagnosis, i.e., where the magnets were placed was not the location, or the sole location, of the pain. In my personal experience with both types of devices, improvements significant enough to make you want to continue using the magnets will be seen in about 60% of the conditions treated. Feet are the most difficult area to effectively treat.

Prices range from about $25 and up for a magnetic strip—permanently magnetized materials embedded in plastic that you can place anywhere and secure with bandages—to $60 or so and up for magnetic wraps and boots all the way to several thousand dollars for an electromagnetic therapy unit with all attachments. Fortunately, the more expensive devices can often be leased so that you have a chance to determine if the effect you get would be worth the investment.

Laser Therapy and LED

Lasers are generators of light waves with all the light having precisely the same wavelength and all waves lined up in parallel bundles. In contrast, natural light is a wide mixture of wavelengths, many invisible, all jumbled together. Lasers are most widely known as a surgical tool or, most recently, as a dentist's instrument. Less intense laser therapy is used to treat, among other things, painful joints. Experiments with lab animals or cells growing in culture clearly show benefits of laser treatment, but it is often difficult to get equally good effects when treating a live, whole horse. Lasers do encourage increased blood flow and more rapid healing of tissues. They are also useful for acupuncture point stimulations and may have some direct pain-killing effects. However, to get these benefits you must pick precisely the right wavelength, frequency, treatment time and treatment schedule. In my experience, it is possible to overdo it and activate too much of an inflammatory response. However, no one seems to be able to agree on exactly what the correct treatment parameters are. Lasers may eventually prove very helpful in controlling arthritis but for now they are best left in the hands of people who are very familiar with their use and have worked out a program that they feel can give consistent results.

Lasers are also very expensive with even the simplest laser costing in excess of $1,000 dollars. However, most companies do have lease arrangements available. If you want to try laser therapy, find an experienced therapist to do the initial treatments. If it is helpful, you can learn the technique yourself (it isn't that difficult to operate) and

147

lease a unit. LEDs use single wavelengths but not parallel waves. They are not as powerful and are basically side-effect free. LED devices provide pain relief for some horses (try before you buy) and are less expensive.

Acupuncture

We still have a limited knowledge of how acupuncture actually works. The Chinese describe it as restoring the flow through energy channels in the body. Modern science notes that acupuncture points are commonly located either over major nerves or in areas where there is a high concentration of nerve endings. Stimulation of acupuncture points causes release of chemicals called endorphins, which are substances with narcotic-like properties.

The major use for acupuncture in arthritis is pain control. There is no guarantee that acupuncture will actually help the horse—some are very responsive to it, others hardly at all. It may be worth a try with conditions that are particularly difficult to control by other means, like foot problems.

Chiropractic Manipulations

Another alternative therapy slowly but surely growing is chiropractic treatments for horses. The principles of chiropractic medicine are essentially that the health of one part of the body can effect the health of another and that all parts are interconnected through the spinal cord. Whether you embrace the theory in total or not, it is certainly true that a painful foot can eventually result in a painful shoulder, painful back, stiff neck, painful opposite leg and the list goes on. Horses most definitely can, and do, develop tension and pain along their spines and in their muscles that could probably benefit from massage and manipulation by someone who really knows what they are doing. The problem is finding that someone.

Quacks, unfortunately, abound in all fields of alternative medicine, and this one is no exception. It is a shame both for the people who get taken in by them and for the legitimate therapists who must suffer from the bad name the entire field may get as a result. However, there is a growing number of genuinely qualified veterinary chiropractors—some veterinarians also—who can help a horse, especially a stiff, older horse. There is an American Veterinary Chiropractic Association that certifies veterinary chiropractors (a 30-hour course) and can provide you with a referral. You can write or call them at: AVCA, Animal Chiropractic Center, 623 Main, Hillsdale, IL 61257, (309) 658-2920, fax (309) 658-2622.

With specific reference to arthritic conditions, chiropractic manipulation will be of value in controlling any secondary malalignments in the spine and surrounding muscles that occur as a result of disease in the lower joints of the legs. Most veterinary chiropractors do not attempt to treat the lower joints of the horse's legs.

TENS

TENS units are familiar to any of you who have ever been hospitalized for a neck, back or muscular problem, or had to have physical therapy. The purpose of the TENS unit is to block pain. Its effectiveness varies, as does the length of time the pain relief lasts, depending on the individual. TENS units work by sending out a mild electrical current in a specific wave form that interferes with the electrical transmission of nerve impulses along pain nerve fibers. TENS can be helpful to horses but is primarily used in younger animals that are in heavy competition. It is too time consuming and technically demanding for regular use on most conditions of older horses, although it could be considered as an interim measure—for example, when trying various approaches to getting a horse with navicular disease under control. Because of the very real danger of making the impulse too intense (painful), TENS therapy is best left in the hands of professionals.

Electrical Stimulation Therapy

In addition to the TENS, there are a few therapy units that employ direct electrical stimulation. The shock is hidden inside a TENS wave so that the horse does not object to the sensation.

When placed over muscles, these units result in extremely strong contractions that can literally move the horse involuntarily. It's an amazing thing to watch. There are also less dramatic devices that provide intermittent very small currents, just enough to barely get perceptible twitching from the muscles. These devices are used in cases of nerve damage to muscles (to prevent the muscles from shrinking) and also during the healing stages of bowed tendons to stimulate the attached muscle and encourage the tendon to heal with fibers in a more functional arrangement. Some companies are trying to sell the idea that electrical stimulation has a place in the treatment of joint disease. There is no solid evidence to support this and nothing about the way the therapy works that even makes sense in trying to use it on painful joints. Steer clear of this one.

Ultrasound

Sound waves have a variety of applications. Some devices penetrate deeply to generate "pictures" of the tissues inside for diagnostic purposes. These work similarly to sonar/radar devices used by the armed forces. There are also surgical-strength sound devices, capable of penetrating and disrupting tissues, some strong enough to explode kidney stones. Microwave ovens are another example of the power of specific sound wavelengths. The devices that concern us here have sound waves, which penetrate to various depths (depending on the type of device used) and have different physical effects. By far the most common ultrasound physical therapy devices primarily provide a level of tissue penetration and heating that gives a soothing effect. Some degree of increased circulation accompanies the heating. Any pain relief, improved mobility or improved healing are secondary

The most common ultrasound physical therapy devices primarily provide a level of tissue penetration and heating that gives a soothing effect. Some degree of increased circulation accompanies the heating.

effects related to improving circulation, not directly caused by this type of ultrasound therapy. There are also ultrasound therapy devices available, primarily in Europe, which do not cause tissue heating, have a longer sound wavelength and are actually absorbed by bones and joints for a more direct healing effect.

Price is a good indicator of what type of effect to expect. The relative inexpensive ultrasound devices ($100 to a few hundred) are the soothing, heat-generating type. The longer wavelength machines cost several thousand dollars.

Cutting-Edge Nondrug Treatments

Treatment of rheumatoid arthritis in humans, a disease where the body's immune system essentially turns against the joints, is frustratingly ineffective. In the most advanced and difficult to treat cases, physicians may turn to drugs that block the immune response, such as methotrexate (a potent anticancer drug) or Cyclosporin A (a drug used to block rejection of transplanted organs). These are always last-ditch methods because the potential side effects of these medications can seriously affect the function of multiple key organs. In short, the drugs may be far worse than the disease. Obviously these are not treatments you can pick up at the local tack shop or drugstore.

Sitting on the shelves of some health food stores is a relatively new arthritis treatment for people that is bound to find its way into the hands of horse owners and trainers eventually. It is sold as a nutritional supplement and claims to be completely free of side effects and to literally cure arthritis in as little as 10 to 15 days with relief of symptoms for one to five years.

The active chemical in this product is cerasomal-cis-9-cetylmyristoleate. Or cetyl myristoleate, a derivative of cetyl myristoleic acid. The compound is a derivative of the same family of anti-inflammatory fatty acid substances we are stimulating when we feed the horse flaxseed oil or meal. It was isolated from strains of mice that are resistant to arthritis by a scientist named Harry W. Diehl. Dr. Diehl took his discovery to pharmaceutical companies but they weren't interested—no big profits to be made from a natural substance. This compound works in much the same way as the toxic drugs described above, by blocking the destructive attack on cartilage by the immune system. However, it is reported to work just as well in osteoarthritis (the type horses get) as in rheumatoid arthritis.

We have no experience with this supplement in horses as yet, and it remains to be seen if it is as free of side effects as they claim. However, this is definitely something to be on the lookout for.

MSM

An older supplement also claiming to have anti-inflammatory and immune-modulating properties is MSM—methylsulfonylmethane. MSM is a cousin to the topical joint medication DMSO and is found in highest natural concentrations in freshly picked, ripe fruits and vegetables as well as raw milk.

MSM is a potent antioxidant, which at least partly explains why some horses respond to this supplement. The antioxidant effect is also anti-inflammatory, and some people have had success in older horses using MSM (dose 10 to 30 grams twice per day) instead of phenylbutazone. MSM is also a source of organic sulfur—the only form the horse's body can use—and can substitute for the sulfur that otherwise can only be obtained from the sulfur-containing amino acids such as methionine, often in rare supply in horse feeds. Sulfur is needed to build strong cartilage and connective tissues. MSM also has the ability to block damage to joint cartilage caused by auto-immune reactions—rheumatoid arthritis. Horses supposedly do not get rheumatoid arthritis, but I have certainly seen horses that fit a description of rheumatoid arthritis more closely than osteoarthritis (e.g., unexplained arthritis, wandering from joint to joint, etc.). Horses definitely can get rheumatoid-like joint reactions as a complication of some infections, including deep-seated, chronic Strep infections. An added benefit of MSM is that it might be able to protect the horse's stomach from the ravages of phenylbutazone/bute if given at least one hour before the bute and continued twice a day at a dose of 10 to 20 grams while on the medication.

There are no guarantees with MSM, but it is such a nontoxic substance it's worth a try, especially if your next move would be to start phenylbutazone.

Herbals and Homeopathics

Herbal therapies and homeopathic remedies can be found in virtually any equine catalog you pick up and in many tack shops as well. They are available for just about anything you can think of—from colic to behavior problems. Many people confuse herbal treatments with homeopathic treatments but they are not the same.

Homeopaths call their medicines remedies. They may indeed be based on herbal formulas, and many are, but can be literally any type of substance. The basic premise is that a substance that causes certain reactions in the body (e.g., onions make eyes water) can be used to relieve those same symptoms (e.g., watery eyes from an allergy or cold) if it is made into a homeopathic remedy. To do this, the homeopathic pharmacist begins with a concentrated extract of the substance and then dilutes it down, usually thousands or even tens of thousands of times, until the resulting remedy is so diluted you cannot detect there is anything even in it. It is not my place to sit in judgement of any branch of alternative medicine. Homeopathy has been around for a long, long time, and there may indeed be parts of it that are successful and worth looking into. At this time, however, there is no officially recognized veterinary homeopathy group you can go to for referral. The most commonly used homeopathic remedy for chronic arthritis is Rhus toxicodendron, while acute flare-ups are usually treated with an Arnica remedy. These can be obtained from any homeopathic pharmacy without prescription and are also available from some health food and alternative medicine catalogs.

Herbal treatments are touted as more natural and safe than drugs manufactured by a pharmaceutical company. In some instances this is true, in others it is not. Herbal medicines are drugs. But most are less potent and slower to act than prescription or even most over-the-counter medications. If they worked as well as regular drugs, they would have been concentrated, purified and turned into regular drugs by drug companies long ago. Many of what are now considered traditional drugs had their beginnings as herbal treatments—aspirin and digitalis just to name two.

Herbs can provide significant relief from arthritis symptoms and older horses seem to be particularly sensitive to them—as they are to other drugs—but trying to find out which work the best, or how they work, is often difficult. Yucca is probably the oldest herbal in use for arthritis in horses. The rationale behind it is that this plant contains substances that are similar to corticosteroids. Another herb that is growing in popularity for arthritis is Devil's Claw. This is said to have anti-inflammatory properties. There are several others commonly used such as Cat's Claw, Angeliga, white willow, ginger, nettle, curcumin and even the common spice turmeric, to name a few. Herbal arthritis products for horses may contain only one extract or a wide mixture of herbs.

The success rate, meaning at least some relief is obvious, is about 60% across the board. An herb that helps one horse may have no effect on another, and there is no way to predict the response. In my experience, Devil's Claw has the best success rates. A good response gives the horse about as much pain relief as a gram of bute.

An encouraging observation is that older horses do seem to be more sensitive to their actions. If you try an herbal, it is reasonable to expect to see some sign of improvement within a week or so, often in three days, but you should give the treatment a good three weeks before deciding if it is helping.

Topical herbal products are also available. These are much gentler to the skin (and your hands) than common arthritis rubs and often work just as well. Liniments/rubs containing Arnica are indicated for flare-ups of arthritis—joints that are acutely hot and painful. Rubs containing Capsicum control pain by depleting the chemical messenger of pain nerves. They generally take about three days to reach full effect.

Traditional Drugs

I put the traditional drug treatments last on the list of treatments because that is where they belong. Gone are the days when your only option was to put your horse on long-term doses of bute for his arthritis or inject his joints periodically with corticosteroids. These drugs do still have a place in treatment of acute flare-ups or new onset arthritis for a day or two until the joint inflammation has been brought under control. However, there are too many effective and safe treatments for arthritis not associated with the significant side effects these drugs have. Remember too that long term use of either nonsteroidal anti-inflammatory drugs like phenylbutazone (bute) or corticosteroids will actually make the arthritis worse and lock you in even deeper to a continuous medication cycle. Think hard before you use them. An ice pack or warm towel may give the horse just as much relief.

PREVENTING SIDE EFFECTS OF PHENYLBUTAZONE

The horse with arthritis that is properly managed will not need as much anti-inflammatory medication, but there may still be times when a short course of phenylbutazone or other drug is indicated. You can protect the horse's stomach and intestines from damage and help control the inflammation by using the supplement MSM. Start MSM 24 hours before bute, at a dose of 15 to 20 grams twice a day. Feed the third dose of MSM one hour before you start bute. Continue feeding MSM, making sure one of the doses is an hour before the daily bute, for as long as you use the drug. If you want to try MSM as a regular anti-inflammatory supplement (it does help some horses), feed at 10 grams twice a day.

SPECIAL SECTION

RINGBONE AND NAVICULAR DISEASE

Two of the most common, most debilitating/crippling and at the same time most difficult to treat degenerative joint diseases of older horses are ringbone and navicular disease. Countless athletic careers have ended, often prematurely, because of these two conditions.

Ringbone, or more accurately low ringbone, is arthritis of the coffin joint—the joint inside the foot between the coffin bone and the second phalanx. In the later stages it is visible on X-rays because

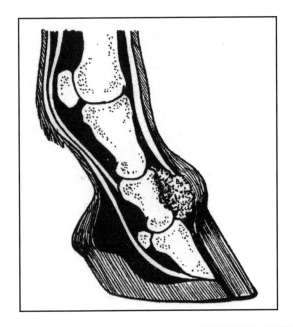

Ringbone is arthritis of the coffin part of the joint inside the foot between the coffin bone and second phalanx.

of the extra bone that is deposited along the dorsal (front) surfaces of the joint. In the early stages this insidious disease is invisible on X-rays and can only be diagnosed by obtaining a sample of the synovial fluid from the coffin joint and testing it for abnormalities indicating inflammation.

Navicular disease affects the same joint but in the plantar (back) area where the navicular bone sits nestled between the coffin bone and the second phalanx. Navicular disease begins as a bursitis, an inflammation of the navicular bursa. The bursa is situated between the back of the navicular bone and the deep flexor tendon. Repeated

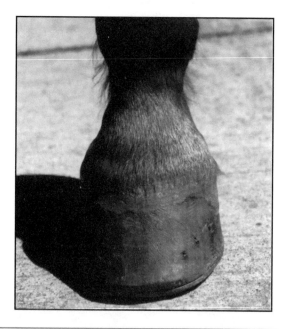

Navicular disease may start because of assymetry in the foot.

compressions of the bursa by the tendon lead to irritation.

This irritation can then spread into the bone itself. Navicular disease may also start because of asymmetry in the foot. The navicular bone is suspended in a sling-like fashion with ligaments that attach to its lateral and medial surfaces—also called the navicular wings. If the horse is not landing perfectly flat, the forces taken by the navicular bone will be greater on one side than the other. This will cause strain and tiny tears in the area where the ligaments attach. These eventually will calcify and become what we call navicular spurs.

Both of these diseases are largely man-made and it is no coincidence that they occur in the same joint. They are caused by trimming horses to have low heels and long toes and also by the tendency for horses wearing shoes to develop feet that are longer than they are wide, a deviation from the naturally round front foot. Both of these practices put tremendous strains on the coffin joint. Particularly devastating for the navicular area is any trimming and shoeing that narrows the width of the heels. All shoes have a tendency to force weight bearing too far front unless they are fit sufficiently far back on the foot to allow the whole heel to participate in weight bearing and sufficiently wide in the heel to allow for normal width of those structures.

A natural foot is not a rigid structure. When the hoof contacts the ground, the force is traveling in a line through the center of the bones. This line ends at a point corresponding with the tip or point of the frog, which should be the exact center of the foot—same distance from the point of the frog out in a straight line to the sides of the foot as there is from the point of the frog out to the toe.

In an unshod foot, as weight comes down over the hoof the wall expands slightly, the frog flattens out, the heels spread and the impact on the bones inside is largely absorbed by an internal structure called the digital cushion. From the outside, a healthy hoof looks like a rock-hard, solid structure, but the impact-absorbing capacity of a healthy frog, heel and digital cushion make it function like well-designed sneakers.

When you put on a shoe, you inevitably lose some of the shock-absorbing capacity of the foot. The frog can no longer touch the ground and very quickly begins to shrink. The heels will often contract very rapidly as well if the heels of the shoe are not fit fully enough. The line of force is shifted forward, away from the point of the frog and more toward the toe. The end result is that the horse becomes deprived of all his natural cushioning. The coffin bone is firmly attached to the hoof wall. When the axis of the foot is changed by lowering the heels and allowing the toe to grow longer than it normally would, the hoof ends up further out in front of the horse than it would normally be and it drags the coffin bone along with it. In the most exaggerated cases, the digital cushion is greatly atrophied and the structures in the back of the foot, especially the navicular, are deprived of this important cushion.

The first area to suffer because of this is the navicular bone for two reasons. First, the cushioning from frog and heel expansion and the digital cushion is lessened. Second, because the line of force is shifted further front, the deep flexor tendon will undergo more stretch and compress the navicular bursa to a greater extent. On the dorsal (front) surface of the foot, you also have the stage set for ringbone to develop. When the heels are low and line of force shifted front, the edges of the coffin bone and the second phalanx are forced

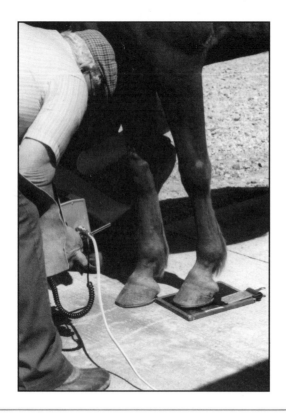

In the later stages, ringbone is visible on X-rays because of an extra bone along the dorsal surface of the joint. In the early stages, ringbone is invisible on X-rays and can only be diagnosed by obtaining a sample of synovial fluid.

closer together. Joint space is lost and irritation occurs.

How long the horse can withstand these abnormal forces depends on how extreme the variation is from what his natural foot would be and also how hard he is worked. However, even lightly used horses will eventually develop some degree of navicular bone change and often some degree of ringbone as well. This is why radiologists expect to see abnormal navicular bones on X-rays taken from horses 10 years old or older and have even come to describe those changes as normal for age!

Treatment

The first step commonly taken in treatment of ringbone and navicular disease is often to change the shoeing. This is certainly the right idea, since shoeing more than likely was a major cause in the first place, but the changes made are sometimes in the wrong direction or only address part of the problem. Raising the heels is a standard first adjustment made with navicular disease. The reasoning is that this will ease the stretching of the deep flexor tendon and take the pressure off the navicular bursa and the navicular bone. This is definitely a step in the right direction but it will only be partially effective unless the horse's toe is also shortened. Shortening the toe will bring the hoof back where it is supposed to be—centered under the column of bones in the foot. The horse may get temporary relief from artificial devices like wedge pads or shoes that are made higher at the heel than at the toe, but the relief won't last.

Rocker motion or rolled toe shoes are another part of the common corrective shoeing techniques for navicular disease and ringbone. They may be used at the same time as the heel is raised or added later on, when the raised heels alone are no longer providing any relief. In fact, rolled toe shoes become an absolute necessity in

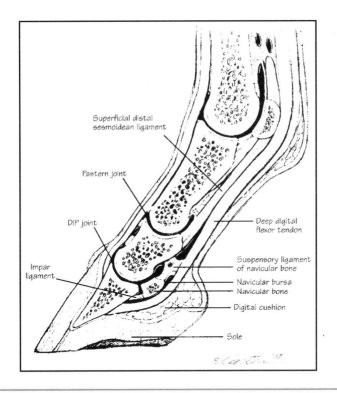

This drawing illustrates the internal structures of the lower leg and foot.

time if steps are not taken to bring back the toe and position the hoof where it is supposed to be—underneath the horse and centered on the column of bones.

The long toe sticking out in front of where it is supposed to be essentially jams into the ground and prevents the horse from breaking over normally. When these horses walk up a hill you can actually see how the toe gets in their way. The beveling/rounding of the toe helps the horse to move over it but does nothing to correct the tremendous strain put on the navicular bone and the pinching together of bones along the top surface of the coffin joint. The higher heels the horse has will relieve some of the pull of the deep flexor tendon when he stands still, but that long toe means it will be just as bad once the horse moves and tries to break over. No shoe can reverse this anatomy—the foot itself needs to be changed.

To picture all of this, look carefully at the drawing on page 165 showing how the internal structures are situated in the natural foot compared to the shod foot. Notice how the joint space at the coffin joint is much more narrow on the dorsal (top) surface than it is at the back, where the navicular bone sits. Notice how the navicular bone is being wedged in against the back of the coffin joint and the deep flexor tendon is pulled thin and tight. The area under the navicular bone should be thick and dense, filled with the digital cushion as it is in the natural foot. In the shod foot the digital cushion is almost nonexistent. Once you have identified and appreciated these differences between the two feet, imagine what happens when the foot is planted flat on the ground, as it is in these drawings, but the horse's leg is now trying to move forward. The coffin bone is not moving. As the second phalanx begins to rotate forward, the dorsal edges of the bones are pinched together even tighter and the stretch on the deep flexor tendon with compression of the navicular bone gets greater and greater. If the horse has a lot of extra toe sticking out in front of his foot, it is going to prolong these moments of greatest compression that result in ringbone and navicular disease.

The solution is to get the horse's foot back into a normal shape. Things like elevated heels, rolled toes and silicone packing in the feet will only work temporarily. They are actually worsening the problem in some respects because they are encouraging the foot to lose more and more of its natural cushioning. Some horses with navicular disease and ringbone are so far gone in terms of degeneration in these joints that nothing is going to help them too much. However, for a large number of other horses, relief of a permanent nature is possible if you change the foot back to the way nature intended it to be.

The first step is the removal of shoes. The very idea of this often horrifies owners, but if this process is done correctly you will be quickly reassured since each trimming makes the horse more comfortable than he was before. By removing the shoes, you allow the frog, heels and digital cushion to receive the natural stimulation that shoes remove. These structures will then become softer, wider and more shock absorbing so that the navicular can regain its natural cushion. To accomplish this, the sole, quarters and heels are left alone—no trimming or paring except what is absolutely necessary to make sure the horse is landing flat. Some horses may also show heels that have actually curled under the feet and are pressing on the soles and frog like an ingrown toenail. These need to be pried out and cut all the way back.

Work is concentrated at the toe. The goal is to bring the toe gradually back to where it should be by filing away at the extra toe on the foot. No toe is removed by nippers. All work is done with the rasp. Many blacksmiths are fearful of doing this and will not get close enough to the white line, but in horses with extra toe all this hoof area is dead and you can file back to and even into what appears to be the white line without encountering any live tissue. Each time the toe is brought back, the horse comes a little closer to achieving natural alignment of the bones and relief of pressure and pull on the deep flexor tendon. When properly done, making sure only to take the toe back 1/4 inch or so with each trimming/rasping session, the foot will begin to resume normal shape and function and the horse will be more comfortable every step of the way.

It takes time for the hoof to adapt. The horse is starting out with essentially no digital cushion, his frog and heels are shriveled and almost worthless for shock absorption and his toe will still be too far out in front of him. He also needs to grow heel but will probably not show much growth until the toe has been brought back to a more natural location.

Until this can occur, the horse's feet will be sensitive. Don't let this transition phase force you back into shoes. Keep the horse off hard ground and road surfaces. Bed him with a deep layer of shavings, straw on top if you like straw. Turn out or walk only where there is a thick growth of grass. You can also relieve temporary soreness (which will be greatest in the heels and back of the foot) by poulticing the feet with poultice that is kept in the freezer for greater cooling effect. Apply Arnica gel or liquid to the coronary band.

Use either medication/poultice boots or a foot sack fashioned from plastic feed bags to hold the poultice in place. Be patient and your efforts will be rewarded in a few short weeks with a horse that is moving more comfortably and likely to stay that way.

The Role of Medication

Anti-inflammatory medications, usually phenylbutazone (bute) are commonly prescribed and used for both ringbone and navicular disease. A better approach is to remove the abnormal pressures that are causing the pain by following the hoof-care guidelines above. Reserve use of bute for those times when the horse is extremely uncomfortable and even then try to get away with a single dose. Devil's Claw extract is an herbal alternative that has the anti-inflammatory effect and pain-relieving effect of a low dose of phenylbutazone in many horses. It's not as dramatic as bute but it does help. Soaking the feet in cold water and/or ice cold poulticing is another alternative.

Many other drugs have been tried over the years in the treatment of navicular disease—ACTH, anticoagulants and most recently isoxuprine. It is interesting to note that most of these are directed at restoring normal circulation. The reason the horse has abnormal circulation in the first place is that his foot is not functioning normally. The natural foot without a shoe has a pumping action with each step. When you eliminate this by getting the bottom of the foot further and further off the ground you are causing poor circulation and worsening the problem. If you are going to try these drugs, use them as a complement to corrective trimming, not as a substitute for it.

Other Therapies

The nutritional support program outlined for treating arthritis may help somewhat with ringbone and navicular disease but probably not as much as with other joints since the problem here is largely mechanical/physical and is not centered as much on joint cartilage per se as it is in the larger joints elsewhere in the body.

Magnetic therapy, both permanent magnetic boots and electro-magnetic therapy, have provided significant relief for a number of horses with ringbone and navicular disease. There are some horses that show no response at all and others that are dramatically improved worsen when therapy stops then dramatically improve again when it is restarted. It is not clear why individuals do or do not respond. It may just be a matter of individual sensitivity to the therapy or may be because there are other things, like sole pain or pain outside the foot, contributing to the degree of lameness. Enough horses respond that it is certainly worth a try. Just make sure you purchase a product with a return guarantee in the event it doesn't help your horse.

Acupuncture and laser therapy have also been tried with these and other causes of foot pain but with variable results and usually only partial relief. It can't hurt to try them but you would probably be better off sticking to the basics of cold soaks, poulticing, corrective trimming, etc.

CHAPTER NINE

HORMONAL
FUNCTION

It's easy to remember which hormone and glandular systems are affected by aging—all of them are. The first one everyone thinks of is reproductive. Sexual desire and sexual function wane with age, but aging involves far more complicated processes that begin in the pituitary gland.

The Pituitary

The pituitary gland sits deep within the brain and is called the mas-

Many horses with Cushing's disease will also have abnormally long and woolly hair coats that do not shed out as they should in the spring.

ter gland—controlling the function of every gland in the body. Basically, the pituitary gland reads the levels of all the various hormones present in the blood. If it detects a low level, it releases what is called a stimulating hormone. This is a specific protein that travels in the blood to the target gland that responds by putting out more of the needed hormone. The pituitary may also release specific messengers in response to high levels of hormones. For example, when the estrogen in a mare's body is at its peak, the pituitary will step in and release the hormone needed to cause the follicle on her ovary to rupture and release an egg. Overfunctioning of the pituitary will usually cause overproduction of hormones, while underfunctioning will result in lower hormone levels than normal.

We do not know of any conditions in horses where the pituitary is underfunctioning. The pituitary gland in horses, and other species as well, seems to retain its ability to function normally well into old age. When decreased functioning occurs during aging, it is usually the result of a chemical change that signaled the pituitary to slow down rather than any failure in the pituitary itself.

Older horses may develop nonmalignant tumors in their pituitary glands (pituitary adenomas) that cause the gland to overfunction and produce a variety of problems. The most common of these is called "Cushing's disease." Tumors in a specific area of the pituitary cause the overproduction of hormones that signals the adrenal glands to put out high levels of corticosteriods—those same potent anti-inflammatory drugs sometimes used to treat arthritis or severe allergic reactions. Corticosteroids are not meant to be present in the body in elevated levels for long periods of time, and this results in a variety of abnormalities. The horse's blood sugar level and level of fats in the blood become abnormally elevated because corticosteroid hormones block the effects of insulin. Like a diabetic person, the horse will develop a voracious appetite and drink abnormally large amounts of water, making abnormally large volumes of urine that test very high for sugar. The muscles become weak and the horse loses weight because the glucose cannot effectively get inside the cells where it belongs.

Electrolyte abnormalities also develop as a result of the high steroid levels, including low potassium which contributes to the weakness and high sodium levels. Most of these horses are also very sluggish and depressed—probably because they feel lousy but also possibly as a direct effect of the high corticosteroid levels, which can cause depression.

Many horses with Cushing's disease caused by adrenal tumors will also have abnormally long and woolly hair coats that do not shed out as they should in the spring. This is probably caused by other hormone abnormalities in addition to the high corticosteroids. In some horses, this tendency not to shed out normally may occur before the other symptoms of full-blown Cushing's disease and could therefore be an important warning sign.

In addition to the high ACTH, corticosteroid and insulin levels, some horses may have abnormal thyroid function. This can be caused either by a pituitary lesion or as a direct effect of the ACTH and the steroids. Insulin itself also has an antithyroid effect.

As you can see, the picture is very complicated. However, the main lesion responsible for all these problems is the tiny tumor in the horse's pituitary. Effective therapy attempts to combat the high ACTH level that caused all these things in the first place while controlling the symptoms.

A variety of drugs have been tried to control the ACTH secretion by the pituitary gland in humans and have also been used but much less extensively in horses. These include o,p'-DDD (older therapy), Pergolide cyproheptadine and bromocriptine. Because of the high blood sugar, these horses are often described as being diabetic. However, because insulin may already be high but its effects blocked, treatment with insulin may not help.

If you have a horse with the symptoms of Cushing's disease and want to try treatment, you may have to contact a veterinary school or large equine clinic to find a vet familiar with the drugs. Interestingly, there is a report in the veterinary literature that says Pergolide treatment can be effective in reversing the depression seen in these horses. Symptomatic treatment involves clipping the horse in warm weather to keep him comfortable, making sure he has lots of the water he needs to keep clearing all that excess glucose from his system, and providing a very high-quality, high-protein diet to help slow down the muscle loss. Feeding supplemental chromium to the horse might make him more sensitive to the insulin and help control blood sugar, but this has not been tested as yet. If the fat levels in the blood get too high, treatment with heparin might be tried to clear this up at least temporarily.

Drug therapy combined with radiation treatments is the approach usually taken in people with these tumors, but radiation therapy for horses is generally not available. Since the disease has a relatively slow onset, horses may continue to do okay for years if you just make sure they are clipped in the spring and have plenty of water. Because of the advanced age of horses with this problem, most people decide against treatment.

The Hormone-Producing Organs

Another factor that may influence hormone levels is the health of the gland or organ that actually produces the hormones. Removing the ovaries (spaying) or castration result in greatly decreased levels of the sex hormones since these organs are the principal place where they are made. The pituitary gland will sense this and send out stimulating hormones, but there will be no response since the organ necessary to make them is no longer there. (Actually, the sex hormones do not really drop completely to zero after these surgeries because there are other sites in the body that are capable of making small amounts of the hormone.)

Sex Hormones and Growth Hormones: With age, the sex organs—ovaries or testicles—gradually slow their production of sex hormones. It is not really clear whether this is caused by factors in the glands, in the pituitary gland or is a more complex reaction that involves other hormones. The most current research seems to favor the latter theory. Decline in sex hormone production appears to parallel declining levels of another very important hormone—growth hormone. Exactly which comes first, and what the specific triggers are, remains a mystery. What we do know is that falling levels of the sex hormones and falling levels of growth hormone, plus another substance related to growth hormone called IGF-1 (insulin like growth factor), are responsible for most, if not all, of the physical changes we see with advancing age, such as increased body fat, decreased muscle mass and decreased metabolic rate.

Veterinarians have been treating lethargic older animals with sex hormones for years—either testosterone or the related synthetic anabolic hormones like Equipoise™ or Winstrol™. Estrogen can also be tried. It has a milder anabolic effect but often is enough to make a significant difference in an older horse. Estrogen has gotten a lot of bad press lately, especially in the human weight-lifting circles where anabolics are a big deal. The fact is, estrogen is an effective anabolic. The negative effects that have been linked to estrogen relate only to when the hormone is taken orally. If it is injected or given through a skin patch, the effects are different. These drugs are effective in temporarily making the seniors stronger, more energetic and more alert. They are expensive, however, and treatments must be repeated every two to four weeks.

A natural alternative that also has beneficial effects is the use of gamma oryzanol, an anabolic substance that is isolated from rice bran. Don't be taken in by claims that plain rice bran supplements have gamma oryzanol. They do, but not enough to effectively treat an insect. Rice bran supplements provide the horse primarily with stabilized fats that do little more than add to his layer of body fat. Even pure gamma oryzanol supplements may actually contain very little gamma oryzanol at all. They get away with this because there is inadequate federal regulation of equine supplements. One brand with proven high gamma oryzanol content and that I personally know works well is Body Builder™. If you want to try another gamma oryzanol product I strongly suggest you call the company that makes it and ask if they can sent you a copy of laboratory tests proving it actually contains as much gamma oryzanol as they claim.

If they refuse, don't buy it. Body Builder™ is effective at 1,000mg a day. Powdered gamma oryzanols must be given at two to four times that amount.

The next fountain of youth drug is probably going to be growth hormone or IGF-1. Trials in people have already reported phenomenal results with the participants returning to levels of strength and muscle mass they had 20 years previously. Even gray hair may be reversed. The problem at the moment is that we don't know if there are long-term side effects and the stuff is incredibly expensive. Once the safety can be confirmed and someone manages to perfect an effective synthetic form, growth hormone is likely to hit the market with a fanfare that makes Viagra pale by comparison.

Thymic Hormones: The thymus gland is a tongue-shaped structure that sits just inside the chest, along the windpipe. The hormones of the thymus gland are critical to normal immunity. These hormones are what make specific types of blood cells, the lymphocytes, turn into either the B cells (antibody producing cells) or the T cells (cells that attack and kill invaders, like viruses or abnormal cells like cancer, directly). Those are the specific cells that the AIDS virus destroys.

The thymus gland hormones also are involved somehow in the release of growth hormone, or vice versa. Levels of thymic hormone take a similar pattern of decline with age as we see with the sex hormones and growth hormone. This undoubtedly plays a role in older horses being more susceptible to infections, parasites and even cancer. What is not completely clear yet is how important it is to the physical changes of aging—specifically weaknesses and loss of muscle. As more becomes known about thymic hormones, we may find it is just as important as growth hormone in preventing aging.

Insulin: Release of the hormone insulin, which controls blood sugar, is a special case. Insulin is released by the pancreas when the horse's blood sugar rises above normal, such as after a meal. Insulin then stimulates cells, like fat cells or resting muscle cells, to take up the excess insulin. If blood sugar drops, insulin also drops. This stimulates cells to break down fat into glucose to get blood sugar back up where it is supposed to be.

Older humans are more likely to develop a type of diabetes called diabetes type 2. However, it is becoming more and more clear that this is not an age-related change that has anything to do with how normally the pancreas functions. It is instead related to lifelong habits of eating high sugar foods, to obesity and also to damage to the pancreatic cells that is caused by chemicals, infections and other free radical damage rather than by the pancreatic cells just getting old. Diabetes is not a big problem for horses of any age (except when associated with pituitary tumors), the primary reason probably being the horse's diet. Even horses fed grain get far more complex carbohydrates than simple sugars in their diets.

However, I have seen a number of horses that have the opposite of diabetes—low blood sugar. This makes the horse very sluggish and has an absolutely devastating effect on any athletic performance. In one of these horses, the blood insulin level was proven to be abnormally high. This was causing too much sugar to be driven inside the cells. This situation is very similar to hypoglycemia in people—

attacks of low blood sugar that make them very weak, even causing them to pass out. In people, the consequence of all this extra insulin floating around is that the cells become desensitized to it. When that happens, the situation begins to reverse and less and less of the glucose gets inside the cells (insulin sensitivity is required for the glucose to enter) so blood sugar gets higher and higher until they eventually have diabetes.

The horses I have seen with low blood sugars all responded to supplementation with the trace mineral chromium. Chromium is known to be required for normal insulin sensitivity in people, and we are gaining more information about it in horses. At this time, however, chromium has not been approved as a supplement for horses and high levels of it can be toxic. If your horse has low blood sugar and you want to try chromium, you will need to find a vet or a nutritionist who is familiar with chromium supplements to write you a prescription and follow up until you find the correct dosage.

Thyroid Hormone: The thyroid gland, like the insulin producing pancreas, also seems to be fairly immune to the ravages of time. While thyroid function does tend to taper off somewhat with age and we are seeing more and more hypothyroidism in horses, it is not necessarily because the thyroid gland itself got old and wore out. There is an increasing number of chemicals being implicated as causes of abnormal thyroid function, chemicals that have really only been around for a relatively short period of time. This includes an assortment of herbicides, pesticides and byproducts of industry. Even diets high in soy and possibly alfalfa may cause depressed thyroid function.

Diagnosing hypothyroidism is often not easy. The recording of early morning temperatures may be more accurate than many blood tests. Determination of T4, the most frequently done test, is probably not of much value. Levels of T3, the active thyroid hormone, will more accurately reflect the true thyroid status. However, even this can be normal if the cause of the problem is a chemical or plant substance that can masquerade as a thyroid hormone. These substances have a chemical structure that is similar enough to thyroid hormone that they can attach to thyroid hormone receptor sites on the body's cells. However, because they are not thyroid hormone, they do not have the same effects on the muscle or whatever organ's cells they attach to. Those cells are therefore starved for thyroid hormone but the brain cannot detect that anything is wrong because the levels of actual thyroid hormone in the blood are normal. Because those blood levels are normal, the usual tests for thyroid function will be normal too. Meanwhile, the horse looks more and more hypothyroid.

For this reason, veterinarians will often treat for hypothyroidism by clinical signs; knowing from experience that the blood tests may contradict what their eyes and the owner's reports are telling them. People are also increasingly switching to dessicated thyroid (dried thyroid gland) rather than synthetic hormones, since the synthetic hormones usually contain only T4 and what the horse needs is more T3, the active form.

The symptoms of hypothyroidism—easy fatigue, lethargy, poor appetite, weight loss or weight gain (depending on the appetite)—are all fairly nonspecific and common in older horses anyway. A more reliable symptom than those above is a below normal or fluctuating body temperature. The horse's normal temperature is about 99 to 100. Horses with low temperature readings in the morning hours probably have at least underactive thyroids. The usual decision is to try thyroid supplementation regardless of what blood tests show.

Exercise and Hormone Levels: Exercise is a powerful stimulator of hormone release. All the hormones associated with lean body mass, decreased body fat, improved metabolism and a sense of well being are triggered by exercise. These include the all-important growth hormone. Studies have repeatedly shown that when older people continue to exercise regularly, they can almost completely prevent the loss of muscle and increased body fat that would otherwise normally go along with aging. This book recommends regular exercise for older horses for other reasons as well. Exercise-associated growth hormone release, and how that will keep your horse stronger, more alert and feeling better, is one of the most compelling reasons not to simply turn the older horse out to pasture.

CHAPTER TEN

HEALTH PROBLEMS OF THE OLDER HORSE

If you follow the suggestions in this book, your horse should have fewer everyday problems that plague older horses and they will be of a milder nature. However, he will not be immortal or invincible. Following are some of the common health problems older horses face.

Tumors and Cancers

Blessedly, cancer is not a major problem in horses. However, advancing age does increase the likelihood of some types of tumors and cancers.

Malignant Melanoma: Malignant melanoma is a tumor that arises in the pigment-producing cells of the skin. It may be triggered in some cases by alterations in melatonin, a hormone produced by the pituitary gland, but this is unproven. Melanomas affect gray horses almost exclusively. They are hard, black rounded growths easily seen and felt under the skin. Ulceration of the overlying skin may occur in some cases. Melanomas in horses do not spread aggressively or quickly. They usually arise around the anus, genitals, and tail region and then grow and spread locally, sometimes extending into the abdomen. There are reports of melanomas in the feet. Serious problems only occur when they are large enough to interfere with passing urine or manure or if abdominal growths result in abdominal pain/colic.

Various treatments have been tried, including herbal remedies, radiation, topical antitumor drugs, cimetidine and vaccines. Radiation does not work on these tumors. Herbal remedies may provide temporary relief of some problems but are not cures. Cimetidine has been reported to induce prolonged periods where the tumor does not grow larger, and topical drugs will sometimes shrink the tumors. Surgery is not used except to decrease the size of tumors whose bulk is causing problems since it is nearly impossible to remove all tumor cells. The vaccines are created using the horse's own tumor cells in hopes of stimulating his immune system to fight back. These are very expensive ($1,000 or more). Results of similar therapy in people are at best a partial response in 50% of the people treated.

Squamous Cell Carcinoma: Squamous cell carcinomas in horses are restricted almost exclusively to the skin. They usually occur at a junction where skin and mucus membrane (e.g., the moist lining of the mouth, eye or genital tract) occur. They are usually thickened but not too prominent lesions that spread out along the area and have a raw, ulcerated surface. Early lesions can be difficult to distinguish from a noncancerous process, but a hallmark is that they will not heal no matter how they are treated.

Squamous cell tumors are most effectively treated by a combination of surgery and radiation. Surgery is done to remove all tumor that can easily be removed, then the area is usually treated by implanting tiny radioactive seeds or pellets.

Lymphosarcoma: Lymphosarcoma or lymphoma is a tumor that involves the lymph nodes and any other areas where lymphocytes (a specific type of white blood cell) may congregate, such as the spleen, liver, skin and along the intestinal tract. In fact, lymphatic tissue is found widely throughout the body and there is no limitation to where this cancer could show up. It usually appears after early middle age in horses, but cases in younger horses are sometimes seen. Lymphosarcoma is relatively uncommon. However, the number of cases of this type of cancer has been rising very sharply in people over the last few years, especially in forms that appear in senior citizens. Some authorities describe it as an epidemic. It is not completely clear yet whether the same is happening in horses, although it is my impression it is becoming more common and there are certainly more papers appearing in the veterinary literature. Attention is being focused on environmental toxins. One of the chemical classes strongly suspected is herbicides—the chemicals used to control weeds in farmers' fields (see Chapter Five).

Lymphosarcoma in people is treated by chemotherapy and radiation therapy but it is a long, harrowing struggle with no guarantees. Because of the severity of side effects and the tremendous cost of treatment, there are no established treatment programs for horses with this disease.

Other Tumors

Mares can develop tumors on their ovaries that require surgical removal, but these are really not more common with old age. In fact, pregnancies often trigger the tumors to grow larger and cause symptoms. Tumors of the testicles are more common in older stallions and often can become quite large without being noticed by the owner. They are usually detected when large enough to cause the horse pain and symptoms of colic.

Benign abdominal tumors called lipomas are seen more often in old horses. They are tumors composed of fat cells that hang by thin stalks and can sometimes become wrapped around a section of intestine causing colic. Treatment consists of removing the tumor and any injured bowel at surgery. This is usually the easy part. Helping an older horse to recover from the stress of a major surgery is a real challenge.

Tumors anywhere, whether cancerous or not, are more likely to appear with age. It is not clear if this is because the chances of genes making a mistake when copying themselves are more common the more times they divide, if exposure to toxic chemicals requires a long period of time to result in a cancer, if infection with cancer-producing viruses takes many years to result in this disease, or if it is the older horse's weakened immunity and decreased ability to recognize and kill abnormal cells that is to blame. In all likelihood it is a combination of these and other factors that explain why tumors occur more often in older animals.

Heart Problems

Horses do not have problems with the same type of heart disease seen commonly in older people—often called hardening of the arteries. This is a tribute to the fact horses consume for the most part an all-natural raw food diet that is low in fat. Horses may develop problems with malfunction of the valves within the heart. In most cases this results in a clear murmur although the horse may appear to be perfectly fine. If symptoms are seen, they are usually in the form of poor tolerance for exercise. Older horses also sometimes show weakening of the walls of the important arteries throughout their body. This can cause arteries to rupture and the horse to bleed to death internally. Horses that suddenly die and assumed to have had a heart attack are usually the victims of a ruptured artery. The muscle of the older heart is also more likely to develop abnormal contraction patterns that cause arrhythmias—abnormal heart rhythms. Again, there may be no symptoms at all or the horse may show very poor tolerance for exercise.

Kidney and Liver Disease

The horse is very rarely the victim of problems caused by failure of the kidneys or liver. That is, there are diseases and infections that can damage these organs but the kidney and liver themselves usually function perfectly well into old age. Even infections of the urinary tract are very rare and usually have an underlying cause. Stones in the kidneys, bladder, ureters (tube from kidneys to bladder) or urethra (tube from bladder to the outside world) are about the only real urinary tract problems horses could have, and even those are rare. Symptoms include straining to urinate, dribbling urine and frequently bloody urine.

Serious viral or bacterial infections can damage the kidneys or the liver. Probably more important though is damage caused by drugs and other toxins. Many common drugs including a wide range of antibiotics, phenylbutazone and overdoses of vitamin D or vitamin K can cause kidney or liver damage. There is also a variety of toxic plants (common cause of liver damage) and fungi contaminating grain. Toxic damage has also been traced to heavy metals, the chemical Dioxin (and probably several other related compounds) and bacterial toxins.

Straining to urinate could be a symptom of a urinary tract problem such as kidney stones.

Lungs

The lungs take a lifetime of abuse from inhaled fumes and chemicals, bacterial infections, viral infections, high pressures during extreme exercise, allergens and wide variations in air temperature. Some decreased lung capacity is to be expected with aging simply as a natural consequence of previous episodes of lung irritation and inflammation over the horse's life. However, even though the old gray mare's lungs ain't what they used to be, you probably won't be able to tell.

Allergies and the eventual problem of COPD (chronic obstructive pulmonary disease), or heaves, characteristically worsens as the horse ages. These conditions cause inflammation resulting in scarring

The problem of COPD (chronic obstructive pulmonary disease), or heaves, usually worsens as a horse ages.

that leaves the horse with less and less lung capacity over time. Advanced lung disease may eventually be a reason for having to euthanize a horse, but there are many things you can do to help arrest the disease and make the horse more comfortable.

Drugs are the most commonly used form of therapy. Bronchodilators, corticosteroids and sometimes antihistamines or specific drugs to help prevent attacks are all frequently prescribed. When flare-ups are severe, antibiotics are usually added routinely as the risk of infection is extremely high. All of these drugs have a very important role to play in controlling chronic lung disease, but management and nutritional approaches work better in the long run. You may still need short periods of drug use if something triggers a serious lung reaction, but your horse's drug requirement will steadily drop unless his lungs have already been so badly damaged there is no turning back.

Management is a very important factor. Every effort should be made to identify those conditions that are usually associated with flare-ups of lung disease. For many, many horses this will be times when they are confined to a barn, especially a closed-up barn. Dust, fumes, allergens from hay/straw/grain and microscopic irritants like mites all build up in the air and trigger problems.

The solution is not to subject any horse with respiratory problems to being in a closed-up barn. You can provide adequate protection from the elements with a three-sided shed without compromising the flow of fresh air. Simply keeping the horse outside is one of the best cures for respiratory conditions ranging from simple chronic, dry, stable cough to wheezing to heaving.

How and what you feed the horse may also influence respiratory problems. Dusty grains or hays are to be avoided at all costs. Allergies to a specific type of grain or hay are unlikely but not impossible. If a horse's pattern of problems suggests a specific type of food is a trigger, by all means stop feeding. Beet pulp-based feeds are often recommended for horses with lung problems. Wetting hay by dunking it in a bucket of water right before you feed it will control dust and mold spores.

The major useful supplements for horses with allergic respiratory problems of any type are the antioxidants, including coenzyme Q10. CoQ10 is also very important in maintaining the efficiency of oxygen-burning reactions in the cells. Aging is associated with a steady drop in the level of CoQ10 manufactured in the body. Supplementation can bring relief of the weakness and shortness of breath on low level exercise these horses may have. Recommended supplementation levels are:

- CoQ10 – 300 to 1,000 mg/day

- Vitamin C 7.5 grams/day

- Grape-seed extract 22 grams/day

- Hesperidin complex 44 grams/day

These nutrients also help increase the horse's resistance to respiratory infections—a common cause of breathing difficulty in older horses. The CoQ10 is by far the most expensive ingredient on this list. You must also be careful to buy a CoQ10 product that is oil based, not a tablet or gelcap with powder inside. CoQ10 is not absorbed very efficiently and you will be wasting your money with the dry forms. Give this mixed in with the horse's flaxseed meal or in a few cc of raw vegetable oil for best effect. The horse may not need the CoQ10 constantly, but I recommend you use it for at least six months.

There won't be any overnight miracles on this program, but you will begin to notice the horse is coughing less frequently in as little as two weeks. After a few weeks there should be a clear improvement in exercise tolerance and how much the horse labors to breathe. You will also notice far fewer runny noses or respiratory infections. Flare-ups requiring drugs will become fewer and fewer, and when you do need drugs you will not need to use them for as long.

THE WAR AGAINST INFECTIONS

Aging can have devastating effects on the horse's immune system. Infections usually bring to mind all the common viral respiratory infections, but it goes far beyond this. Bacterial infections become more common sequelae to minor skin injuries, in the sinuses, in the feet and even along the respiratory tract. Opportunistic infections—infections that would not be able to take hold in a healthy horse with a vigorous immune system—take hold much easier, including various fungal infections and protozoal infections like EPM. Even vaccines will be less effective if the horse's immune system is not functioning in top form.

A high-quality diet, easily digested, is at the heart of maintaining a vigorous, healthy horse with a good immune response. Protein quality is especially important (see Chapter Three), as are the trace minerals, antioxidants, vitamin C, vitamin A, vitamin E and the B vitamins. Boosting these substances after an infection occurs is helpful, but not nearly as effective as making sure the horse has a healthy immune system to prevent the infection taking hold in the first place. Have you ever had a horse with an infected wound or a respiratory infection that seems resistant to many types of antibiotics? This usually isn't because the antibiotics aren't working or the organism involved is some type of super bug. It is because the horse's immune system is not functioning correctly. No antibiotic or vaccine can take the place of a good immune system.

There are a few prescription injections on the market to boost a horse's immune system. The problem with these is that they act in the same way as vaccines, just aren't as specific. Basically, the horse is injected with a substance that is irritating to his immune system in hopes it will alert the cells and make them more active. The problem with these is that if the immune system is not healthy it will not respond any better to this type of immune booster than it would to a real vaccine or an infection.

There are an increasing number of immune-stimulating supplements appearing on the market. One of the oldest is the herb Echinacea. This plant contains long chain sugar molecules that have a specific stimulating effect

$\longrightarrow$

on the killer cells of the immune system. A more recent addition is the substance larch arabanogalactan—another long sugar molecule very similar to those found in Echinacea. It is purified from the larch tree. You can purchase either the larch arabanogalactan as a pure powder to be added to the feed or in a pelleted form where it is combined with other nutrients essential to immune health (Immune One pellets). Both larch arabanogalactan and another new immune stimulant supplement called Actimune also work by improving the local immunity along the intestinal tract. This prevents harmful bacteria and yeast species from multiplying to dangerous numbers and releasing harmful toxins or directly invading the body. This is in addition to their body-wide stimulating effects on the immune system.

Last, but far from least, is one of my favorite immune stimulating substances—whey protein, or the new supplement, GlutaSyn. The important amino acids and other substances in these milk-derived protein supplements are potent supporters of the horse's immune system. They are also very well accepted by the horse, very easy to digest and safe.

A word of caution is in order for the newest immune stimulating substances (whey excluded). Because they have a stimulating effect on the immune system, there is the potential to aggravate any autoimmune or allergic conditions the horse may have. This potential will vary from product to product and depend upon the exact nature of the horse's problem. This is because the different products stimulate different parts of the immune system. If your horse has any chronic health problems, including arthritis, hives, heaves, etc., you should thoroughly discuss the choice of an immune stimulant with your veterinarian before using it.

Intestinal Tract

Choke: Choke is a problem limited almost exclusively to older horses. Choke is the term used to describe food getting stuck in the esophagus between the throat and the stomach. It is often caused or at least made much more likely by tooth problems that prevent the horse from chewing normally and may keep him from drinking normally. It is also caused by a failure to provide constant access to clean water 24 hours a day and at a comfortable temperature. Choke is also probably related to abnormal function of the throat and esophagus. It is suspected the nerves that control swallowing and movement of food can become damaged or at least less efficient as the horse ages.

You may hear some types of food are more likely to make a horse choke—like pellets or hay cubes. However, it is not the physical form of the food that is to blame but the fact it is very dry and the horse didn't take in enough water with it. Choke is best prevented by matching the horse's diet to the condition of his teeth (see Chapter Three and Chapter Eleven). Horses that choke frequently should be fed small frequent meals with a high water content.

Symptoms of choke include standing with the head very low, drooling of saliva and possibly convulsive throat movements, as if trying to vomit. If the horse is kept very quiet, the blockage may pass on its own. Remove anything the horse could attempt to eat (although he probably won't), and leave only fresh water in the stall. In the meantime, call the vet, since if the horse doesn't pass the stuck food down on his own, he will need treatment to prevent permanent damage to the esophagus. Wait no longer than 30 minutes to call the vet. Call immediately if the horse really seems to be distressed.

Colic: Repeated bouts of colic frequently plague older horses. The most common cause used to be damage to the intestines from parasites, but with today's modern wormers this problem can be avoided by a regular worming schedule. Tumors in the abdomen are another cause of repeated colic problems, as are abscesses. The horse may carry abscesses around with him in his abdomen or chest that originally came from an infection he had as a foal. Once a wall forms around an abscess, there is no indication at all the horse has an infection (even on blood work). Abscesses will continue to grow at a slow rate throughout his life, and only when they reach some pretty large sizes do they begin to cause unmistakable symptoms of pain. Basketball size abscesses have been found in older horses. Tumors and abscesses can only be effectively handled by surgery, if the horse is deemed to be an acceptable surgical risk.

More common than any of these causes is colic caused by poor digestion. Any one or combination of the factors contributing to decreased digestive efficiency detailed in Chapter Three can have this effect. Regular dental care will eliminate one cause. Feeding the horse a high-quality diet in frequent small meals is also helpful in controlling colic of this cause. By all means make sure either the grain mix contains a broad range of probiotics or you use a probiotic supplement of at least yeast and bacterial fermentation products. Never make sudden changes in an older horse's diet; introduce new feeds or hays at a rate of only a pound or two a day substituted for the old one.

Last but definitely not least is water intake. Sluggish intestines predispose the horse to some degree of constipation. If water intake is not adequate, this can easily change to full-blown obstruction and if severe enough can mean the horse needs surgery. This is too high a price to pay for not making sure the horse gets and drinks enough water.

Vision

If horses experience a change in vision that is associated with aging (similar to people needing reading glasses when they hit the age of 40 or so), we don't know about it and it certainly is not enough to impair their function. There are a few minor changes that can be detected on examination of the interior of the eye with an ophthalmoscope but, again, these do not appear to have any significance at all in terms of the horse's vision. Old age cataracts do not occur in horses like they do in people.

There is one disease that is not related to age per se but does get worse as time goes on—periodic ophthalmia, or moonblindness, also known as ERU (equine recurrent uveitis). We really don't know what triggers moonblindness, although many theories have been proposed over the years. It is a condition in which the horse's body forms antibodies against the tissues of its own eye. The best theory is that in susceptible horses an infection (viral, bacterial or parasitic) somehow triggers this process. The disease characteristically has times when the eyes are fairly quiet and times when a massive inflammatory reaction flares up, often causing permanent scarring each time. It was felt long ago that these cycles occurred according to the stage of the moon and that is where the condition got the name moonblindness. There is a much higher incidence of moonblindness in Appaloosas and other horses of color with Appaloosa bloodlines but it can strike any breed. The same parasite that causes summer dermatitis, Onchocerca cervicalis, has been implicated in causing periodic ophthalmia, as have other eye area parasites and a variety of micro-organisms. No one single type of infection has been identified. Allergy and vaccine reactions may also play a role in causing this disease.

Treatment involves eliminating any parasitic problems with ivermectin, treating any bacterial infections with the appropriate antibiotics and using corticosteroids to treat flare-ups of the condition as they occur. The horse should be protected from obvious irritants like strong sun, high wind, flies and blowing dust. The supplement MSM, an organic source of sulfur important for the integrity of many structures in the eye, has been recommended for horses with this problem. Suggested dose is 10 grams twice a day for two to four weeks and during flare-ups and 10 grams once a day for maintenance. Also suggested are:

- Vitamin C 4.5 to 7.0 grams daily
    Boosts immune system, strengthens capillaries

- Bioflavinoids (hesperidin complex) 20,000+ mg/day
    Complements vitamin C, strengthens capillaries

- Grape-seed extract, minimum 600 mg/day
    Potential anti-inflammatory, antioxidant; strengthens capillaries

- Vitamin A, use natural sources (carrots, alfalfa)
    The most important vitamin for vision

None of these therapies are intended as cures, including the traditional drug therapies, and there is very little chance that supplements will eliminate the need for drugs during flare-ups but may be helpful in keeping inflammation to a minimum and hopefully in decreasing the number of attacks.

CHAPTER ELEVEN

MANAGING THE
VERY OLD HORSE

If you have ever had a very old horse in your care, you already
know what a challenge they can be. If you are only considering
or facing the prospect of caring for an advanced-years senior, you
definitely need to be prepared for their special needs.

NUTRITION

Getting adequate energy into the geriatric horse is the biggest problem. Many have lost some, most or even all of their teeth. Appetite

Star, to the right, an Arabian Morgan cross, lived outside year round and still enjoyed just 'being a horse' with his 10 years younger companion. Star had to be euthanized at the age of 34 because of complications of a hip/pelvic injury that were making it too difficult for him to get around. Cindy Foley, of Warners, New York, owned Star for 23 of those years. Despite having essentially no teeth, Star's body condition and energy levels were kept up by using a combination of senior feeds, chopped forage protein/mineral supplements, probiotics and joint supplements to maintain his flexibility. A high-quality diet in easy to chew and swallow form is the key.

is usually not great either. Making the situation worse is the fact that their intestinal tract is more easily upset and does not function as well as a younger horse's. These are major problems but not unsurmountable.

Dental Care: Dental care becomes more important with each passing year. You may not be able to save your horse's teeth but you can certainly prevent dental problems from interfering with his eating. Keep the teeth free of gum- and tongue-damaging sharp edges by floating as often as it takes, usually at least twice a year. Damaged teeth should be removed immediately. Pay careful attention to detection of any abnormal odor to the horse's breath—this almost always signals dental/sinus infection. Decreased grain and hay intake, weight loss, decreased water intake (and the varying degrees of constipation these can cause) are also indirect indicators of decreased intake.

Types of Feed: For horses that are just missing a few teeth and are having difficulty chewing their feeds, the diet recommended in Chapter Three can still be used but with some modifications. Grass is preferable to hay since it is easier to bite off and chew (not to mention more nutritious). Try to buy hays cut early in their growth. They will also be much easier to chew. Grains or grain mixes will need to be processed by rolling, steam rolling, crimping or cracking (depend-

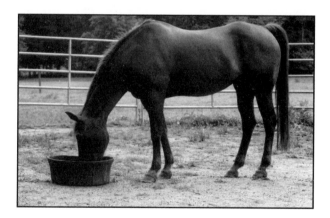

Older horses may need to be fed separately since they may not be able to compete for food in a herd.

ing on the grain type) for easier digestion. You will be able to tell how well the horse is digesting his grain by how much of it turns up in a recognizable form in the manure. Ideally, there should not be any. Make sure your commercial grain mix contains both yeast and bacterial fermentation products. These substances encourage the growth of normal and beneficial microorganisms in the intestinal tract. Both yeast and bacterial species are needed. If your grain does not contain them, provide them separately but mixed in well with the grain.

As the horse ages and loses more teeth, it will become more difficult for him to eat normal hays and even grasses. The problem is both in biting them off and in chewing, but it's the biting off part that is most difficult for horses that lose front teeth. It's fine to feed the horse a few pounds of fresh grass clippings (no fertilizers or other chemicals, though) but you won't be able to provide enough to meet all the horse's needs, and this is certainly a time-consuming way to get nutrition into your horse. A substitute that works well for many older horses is commercial forage products. These are chopped hays of a variety of types that come bagged and definitely cost more, but you won't be saving any money feeding a form of hay the horse cannot use. These products are also often difficult to find. If you have access to the Internet, try a search engine using terms like chopped, roughage, and hay. Some companies that make these products include Lucerne and Equine Specialty Feeds (Triple Crown). Check with your feed or tack stores to see what might be most readily available.

The inability to efficiently digest even processed (crimped, etc.)

grains and chopped hays eventually strikes many horses who make it to a ripe old age. The horse's appetite has probably dropped off pretty sharply by this point as well, so coming up with something that is both palatable and that he can take in sufficient volume to hold his weight becomes a serious problem. There are a variety of pelleted or extruded (puffed up feeds; like those big chunk dog foods) complete feeds for older horses that can be softened with water or even made into a soupy mash if that's all the horse can effectively manage. As much as I personally dislike artificial horse feeds, it certainly beats not getting enough nutrition into the horse. These products contain enough fiber to keep the intestinal tract healthy and a vitamin, mineral and probiotic package designed for older horses.

A variety of additives may be mixed into the feed of an older horse to encourage the appetite. Some are better than others.

An alternative to the complete feeds is a moistened or wet mash feed made from 25% wheat bran, 25% beet pulp, 25% alfalfa hay cubes and 25% grass hay cubes (or 50% hay cubes that are mixtures of alfalfa and grass). For each four-pound batch (one pound each) of the above, add 1/4 pound of molasses, 1/2 pound of cold-processed flaxseed meal (The Missing Link from Designing Health) and one ounce of plain salt. This mixture is balanced in terms of the major minerals calcium, phosphorus and magnesium; all the salt needed for one day in moderate weather conditions; half a day's worth of protein (including essential amino acids); about 1/3 of the day's required copper, zinc and manganese (slightly more on the manganese), and 1/3 of the day's calorie requirements for a 1,000-pound horse. Whether you feed three of these tablespoon batches a day or make up the difference with a high-quality complete senior horse feed, you will have an excellent diet for the toothless or near toothless senior.

You will need to experiment with the complete senior feeds to find the one your horse likes best.

There is tremendous variation between products in taste—at least going by how individual horses either love or refuse to touch any given particular brand. Don't despair if your first try is a flop. Palatability can also be improved by using grated or blenderized carrots or apples, fresh grass, bananas, grapes or some other particular favorite. Some horses love peppermint and a drop or two of the extract (don't overdo it) in the softened feed might work. Uckele Animal Health makes a raw oil that is a mix of coconut and soybean oil. Most horses love the taste and smell. Before you begin adding the tempting taste options, try them out on the horse. If he won't eat a piece of banana from your hand, he won't go for it in his feed either. Do not use any processed human foods or table sugar.

Obviously it takes more time to make your horse meals, but that is only part of the battle. You also have to ensure he actually eats enough of this stuff and that it is not left around too long to ferment. In hot weather, these high moisture dishes can start to go bad within two hours or so.

Hopefully you can come up with a combination that the horse relishes so he will eat enough to hold his weight. If not, the only option left is really to boost the calorie content of the diet by using fat. In fact, many commercial senior diets do use more vegetable fat

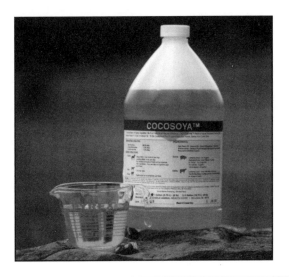

An unbeatable advantage of supplementing feed with coconut/soybean oil mix is that horses love the taste.

than standard horse diets. If at all possible, try to avoid this and definitely go the extra mile and use only raw, unprocessed vegetable oils (see Chapter Three) and never prilled fat products. Prilled fats are specially processed granular forms of lard. Bulk food suppliers can direct you to a source of unprocessed vegetable oils. If that fails, try contacting one of the big manufacturers of salad and cooking oils for people. They will be able to tell you where they buy their bulk unprocessed oils. Flaxseed oil is the best but is far too expensive to use just to supplement calories. Unprocessed soybean oil, canola oil, corn oil, safflower, sunflower, rice bran or sesame oils are all good companions to the cold-processed flaxseed meal. Depending on your location, one or more of these oils should be available without too much trouble. Of all the oils on the list, corn oil will probably be the easiest to find. Raw/unprocessed corn oil even turns up now and then in some of the large tack and supply catalogs, or you could check with a local natural foods store for possible sources. Uckele Health and Nutrition in Blissfield, MI, sells a mixture of soybean and coconut oil that is unfiltered and naturally preserved because all those solids the processing procedure takes out contain very large amounts of natural vitamin E that keeps the oils from going rancid. The coconut oil component is not the healthiest choice in terms of essential fatty acids but, when you average it out with the soybean oil and consider the input from the flaxseed meal, the end result is a very balanced package. An unbeatable advantage of the coconut and soybean oil mixture is that horses absolutely love it (so do dogs, cats, chickens and just about any other animal I've ever seen get close to

Turning a horse into a large field will not compensate for a formal exercise program.

the stuff!). It has a caramel-like aroma and color. I haven't found a horse yet that didn't really like this oil.

A cup of this oil will provide about 25% of the horse's required calorie intake for the day. Some people actually need to feed this much to make up the difference between what the horse should be eating and what he can actually be convinced to take in. Try to gauge how much the horse is leaving uneaten compared to his calculated needs. If he is leaving 25% of what you feed him in a day, you need one cup of oil. If he only leaves 10%, you need about $6^1/_2$ ounces of oil per day. Divide the total intake equally between feedings. Start any oil supplementation gradually, about two ounces per day to start; increasing by about one ounce total more each day to desired level.

Supplements: Supplement recommendations in Chapter Four should also be followed for the very old horse. High-quality B vitamin supplements become increasingly important as the horse's digestive tract becomes less efficient. Pelleted vitamins are usually the easiest to get the horse to eat and can be added to soft feeds since they break down easily. There are also some very palatable liquid multivitamins. When using soft feeds, add the vitamins last and make sure you are feeding the horse an amount he can be expected to consume in a reasonable amount of time (say 20 minutes or so) to avoid losing vitamin potency.

Routine Care: As the horse ages, he becomes more fragile. He is more likely to get sick, and any sickness may be more severe and take longer to recover from. Any form of stress is likely to be much more significant for the very old horse—anything from a sudden nasty turn in the weather to a stone bruise or kick from a friskier pasture mate.

Don't expect the very old horse to hold his own in a group. Odds are he will go downhill in record time if you do. The old horse simply cannot compete effectively and is an easy mark for any bully. His life will be miserable as the other horses act out the eons-old process of excluding the weak and infirm and leaving them to die. It's harsh but it's instinct and you are not going to change that.

The older horse ideally should have his own quarters and his own turnout facilities. If that is not possible, at a bare minimum he must have a protected area where he can be fed several times a day and where you

An unwelcome consequence of aging, that exercise can help avoid, is the replacement of muscle mass by fat.

can protect him from the weather. Shelter needn't be fancy, just effective. A converted 12'-by-12' storage shed with a high and wide enough doorway fitted with an elastic stall guard at the door will work just fine. Even a three-sided shed in a corner of the field that is boxed off with some additional fencing or a few posts and no sag gates would be perfect. The point is you must devise some way to give the advanced senior the protection and extra care he needs. If you are not going to do that, it's not fair to keep the horse.

Avoid at any cost overcrowded or heavily used paddocks/fields which pose a parasite threat and exposure to large numbers of horses who may carry with them infectious diseases. The program outlined in this book is designed to keep the older horse his healthiest and most disease resistant, but there's a limit and immune function will decline over time. Deworm on an effective but not excessive schedule and follow all precautions. Vaccinate for the essentials only.

Last but far from least, don't skimp on mouth and foot care. These are two extremely common sources of pain for older horses and are completely preventable by good routine care.

My Guy, age 20, is a good example of how the correct level of exercise, combined with dietary adjustments have worked together to prolong a horse's useful life.

CHAPTER TWELVE

PURCHASING AN OLDER HORSE

The search for that special horse is fun and exciting. It can also be exhausting, time-consuming, and expensive. When you do finally locate a horse with the right chemistry and a price match, a wise buyer should make every effort to determine if the horse is truly suitable.

For most people, prepurchase scrutiny is limited to a veterinary examination (often less than complete), a few minutes on the horse's back and whatever information can be garnered from the sales pitch. This method, however, leaves much room for improvement.

The veterinary examination is a key element and will be discussed in detail later. Your veterinarian will examine the horse for medical illnesses and can help you decide if tests such as X-rays are necessary. Cutting corners on the veterinary examination could ultimately cost more than the fees you save, particularly with an older horse that is more likely to have problems.

TRYING OUT THE HORSE

Very few people would buy a horse without riding him first, but this contact is usually too brief to be of much value. In addition, the horse is frequently shown by a professional who knows him well and has worked out the kinks before you arrive.

If at all possible, try to get the horse on trial for a few days before you buy. Failing this, make sure you ride the horse at least twice and under different conditions. For example, if the first trial was in midafternoon, in a ring, and after the seller had put the horse through his paces, return early in the morning to hack the horse cross-country (or at least in a field). Request that he not be ridden, longed, or turned out before you ride. An exception to the turnout requirement might be made for a horse that is normally kept turned out. It could be very useful to see if the horse becomes stiff or very unmanageable when confined even overnight, particularly if your management of him will include stabling. By riding the horse twice, you increase your chances of detecting any lameness or behavior problem and generally get to know the animal better.

216

Ride a horse more than once, under different conditions and at different times of the day, before you decide whether or not to buy him.

Bad Habits

You should also be aware that the horse may come with a set of similarly deep-rooted idiosyncrasies or vices. He may buck if you use a web girth, throw himself down in streams, or try to destroy the trailer at every red light. Make it a point to observe firsthand as many things about the horse as you can. Be in the barn when he is tacked up, observe him on pasture, watch him at shows or in the hunt field. Most important, ask a lot of questions.

Inquire specifically if he kicks, bites, rears, hauls poorly, breaks out of the pasture, cribs, eats fencing, destroys his blankets, rushes through doorways, hates dogs, has a morbid fear of cows or mailboxes. The seller is unlikely to volunteer such information and can-

217

not be accused later of misrepresenting the horse unless specific inquiries were made. Be very certain you can live with any bad habits or quirks an older horse has since any number of attempts have probably already been made to eliminate them.

LEARNING THE HORSE'S HISTORY

There are several other key pieces of information you should obtain before buying a horse. These include past and present activity levels, illnesses and/or lamenesses, routine health care and diet, and shoeing requirements.

Past and Present Activity Levels

An aged horse's performance history may include numerous championships or years of brilliant performance at the activity you desire of him, but this alone has little or no bearing on his present usefulness. You need to assess his present ability to perform at the level you desire. Regular exercise is vitally important to maintain an older horse's muscular, cardiovascular, and joint fitness. If he has lost considerable body condition you may never be able to restore him to his previous level of activity or proficiency.

It is a good rule of thumb to be extremely cautious about buying an older horse that is not currently performing at a level equal to or greater than what you will require and never to buy a horse just coming off turnout. It is virtually impossible to predict if a horse

When you find an older horse that you are considering buying, it makes sense to first get a thorough examination by a veterinarian.

that has been turned out will hold up to training; even the veterinary examination is of little help here if you will require a drastic change in his activity level.

Medical History and Diet

A horse's past management is also of vital importance. The vaccination history will allow you to plan for immediate administration of necessary boosters, if any, and to appropriately schedule the next series. The deworming history is important for the same reasons and will also indicate potential problems. Any horse with a questionable or obviously inadequate deworming history should immediately have a fecal examination. Such a horse may require special isolation and deworming treatments before he can safely be integrated into your regular farm routine without contaminating other animals or the premises. He is also more likely to suffer from parasite-related damage to the intestines and their blood supply, leading to chronic colic and digestive difficulties. This is a significant problem at any age but can be seriously debilitating for the older horse. It is always advisable to get the details of a horse's diet so that changes can be made gradually. Older horses are particularly intolerant of feed changes (grain or hay), and this sensitivity is often compounded by

Midnight, a 20-year-old Morgan Cross, is a beautiful example of an older horse in his prime.

a lifetime exposure to parasite damage. If a horse is receiving any special supplements, ask why. These can often be eliminated or another product substituted with no ill effects. Be alert to any great discrepancy, between a horse's condition and his diet. The thin horse receiving a generous amount of grain could have any number of underlying medical problems, as could the fat or bloated horse on starvation rations. Although this may prove to be only an individual variation in an otherwise normal horse, your veterinarian will be alerted to check for other signs of disease.

You should also commit yourself to an exhaustive effort to uncover a horse's past medical history. This information is immensely useful to the veterinarian performing your prepurchase examination. It will help him or her to focus special attention or testing on previous problem areas and to better evaluate the significance of the current examination findings.

The past medical history will help your veterinarian to diagnose and treat problems the horse may develop in the future should you buy him.

There are three main sources for this information:

1. Recollections of present and past owners

2. Farm health records

3. Veterinary records

The first category is the least likely to be reliable, both for completeness and accuracy, but may contain data not otherwise available. Detailed questioning is needed. Ask about all the major organ systems in detail and try to obtain information from the present owner, trainer and groom, as well as past owners and caretakers.

The following is a list of suggested questions arranged by organ systems.

1. SENSES

    a. Vision

        Is there any history of shying, jumpiness, bolting, twisting over jumps, reluctance to move from bright to dark areas or vice versa?

    b. Hearing

        Is the horse ever startled by your presence when you

Before buying a horse, ask the owner about her history. Is there a history of lameness? Does the horse have allergies? Has he had colic?

come into sight from the rear or side? Does he respond when other horses whinny at feeding time or from the pasture?

2. GASTROINTESTINAL

a. Teeth

Does he drop his feed, throw it around, salivate heavily into the feed tub or pass whole grain in his manure? Does he salivate heavily when a bit is in his mouth? (Simply playing with the bit, or heavy salivation if the horse is a puller, does not necessarily mean there is a problem with the teeth.)

b. Intestines

Has he ever had colic? How often? Is there any history of diarrhea? Does he react badly to deworming drugs (often a sign of heavy parasite loads)? Is he a hard or easy keeper?

3. HEART/LUNGS

Does he sweat or blow unusually hard or long after work? Is he hard to condition? Does he ever cough in the barn? How often does he have respiratory infections? Is there ever a heavy or other than clear nasal discharge? Does he ever breathe hard at rest? Have you ever been told he has a murmur, allergy or heaves? Have you ever heard, or been told, he has a noise with breathing?

4. MUSCULAR

Has the horse ever tied up or had dark urine after exercise? Is there any history of back or flank tenderness?

5. URINARY

Does the horse ever strain to urinate or pass discolored urine? If a gelding, is there any history of excessive behavior of dropping the penis? If a mare, is there an unusual amount of winking or squirting urine, even when not in heat?

6. SKELETAL/JOINT

Is there any stiffness in the morning or before work? Is there any marked preference for one lead or one posting diagonal? Is there any history of lameness? Does the horse wear special shoes (and why)? Have there been any leg injuries? Are there any known recent leg problems? Is there a history of foot abscesses or cracks?

7. REPRODUCTIVE (IF NEEDED OR APPROPRIATE)

Stallion: Number of mares bred per season? Breedings per mare? Conception rate?

Mare: Number of foals? Date of last foaling? Years barren (bred but no conception, early loss of pregnancy)? Years open (not bred)? Any known infections or injuries?

Next, ask if the seller has kept written health records and if you may have a copy.

Finally, identify the veterinarian currently caring for the horse and those past owners have used, as well as any hospitals or clinics where the horse was treated. Ask the owners if they will sign a release form so that the records (or copies) can be turned over to your veterinarian. The release form itself can be simple: "I authorize the release of all medical records for the horse _____ to Dr. _____."

Legally, the owners can authorize the release of the records to anyone they choose, including themselves or directly to you; however, such transfers tend to go more smoothly from doctor to doctor.

Such information is extremely valuable, both before and after purchase. It is unreasonable to expect any older horse to be completely free of problems. The weight you attach to any given difficulty will depend upon the use you have in mind for the animal and/or the degree of risk you are willing to assume. For example, a horse in the early stages of chronic lung disease may have periods during which his breathing is completely normal, and even an examination of his chest by the veterinarian will be within normal limits. If you look at the horse during such a period and do not ask detailed questions about his respiratory fitness, you could easily be buying a hidden problem. Such a horse must be expected to have some degree of difficulty down the road, with associated treatment costs and loss of use. If you know of the problem before purchase, you can take the time to become familiar with the implications of owning such a horse.

Even the most carefully conducted questioning will leave gaps. However, with the answers you receive, the veterinary records, and the history obtained from past owners, a fairly reliable medical profile can be constructed.

It is no secret that most people do not go to such lengths to investigate their potential purchases, and the seller may be surprised by all the questions and special requests. However, there is no reason for the seller to withhold the above facts or resent your questions as long as he is not approached in a hostile or suspicious manner. Anyone who absolutely refuses to comply with your requests for information may be covering up a significant problem.

THE VETERINARY EXAMINATION

Once the horse's medical history data is compiled and you have ridden and examined the horse under a variety of circumstances, proceed with the veterinary examination. There are two opposing schools of thought regarding the prepurchase examination for an older horse. One holds that you must expect some physical problems and therefore a prepurchase examination should be very rigorous and unbending. The other likewise acknowledges an increased like-lihood of problems but claims that scrutiny should therefore be less critical than for a younger animal. There are solid considerations on both sides, and the person who attempts to rigidly follow either is doing a disservice to the veterinary examination.

The guidelines for a prepurchase examination (soundness exam) are basically the same for a horse of any age. It is vitally important to realize the examination cannot do more than inform you of any deficits present on the day the horse is examined. This is why you

Four members of Barbara Madill's family have ridden the 22-year-old Arabian, G Dandy, and placed in the New Jersey 100-mile competition on him.

must make every effort to obtain the background information on performance, routine health care and previous medical problems discussed earlier. (Provide the veterinarian with a list of the questions you have asked and their answers at least one day in advance so that tentative decisions can be reached about areas to be X-rayed or given other special evaluation.) Even with an extensive chronicle and a free hand to perform any indicated tests, your veterinarian still cannot, and should not, guarantee future performance.

This qualification does not mean that the prepurchase examination is unimportant. An aged horse is analogous to a used car. Every effort should be made to avoid investing in an animal that will not reach your expectations and has little ultimate resale value. You may have to accept some battle scars that make him a less-than-perfect physical specimen, but that decision should be based on a thorough and systematic examination.

A complete examination consists of several stages. The horse should be examined at rest, while jogging in hand or on a long line, and under saddle. When under saddle, he should be observed during and after a workout that approximates the activity level you will expect of him. In some cases, this may require the veterinarian to conduct the examination over more than one day. While such scheduling may be difficult, skipping any part of the exam could yield false results.

The following is a description of the examination your veterinarian will perform and the areas that require special attention. You can check a number of these things yourself. By taking a close look on your own, you may be able to eliminate an unsuitable horse without the expense of the veterinary examination or pick up some things you would like the veterinarian to investigate.

Every good examination begins with a system. If you always use the same sequence in inspecting the various areas of the horse, the chance of missing something is greatly decreased. A good working system would be the following:

1. Observe the horse from a distance.

2. Examine the body from head to tail: head, neck, chest; near side; belly; hindquarters; far side.

3. Examine legs and feet: near and far front, near and far hind.

4. Observe the horse in motion.

There are some practical reasons for following this routine. For example, by beginning with the head and neck, you will have sufficient time to accustom the horse to being examined and also get a feel for his personality and stable manners from a safe vantage point. (Remember, the horse has not been foaled that never kicks!) Next, by placing examination of the body before the limbs, you force yourself to pay adequate attention to the whole horse instead of skipping to the part most people find particularly absorbing: the legs. It is also wise to examine the front and hind legs together so that subtle differences from right to left will be more obvious. Be aware that the horse may become a little agitated with the sequence of the leg examination if he is used to having his feet picked in the order of near front, near hind, far hind, far front. Finally, it is logical to proceed to watching the horse move immediately after noting any questionable areas on his legs.

Observation from a Distance

Step one, observation from a distance, should be done when the horse is loose in his stall or turned out, not while he is being held or cross-tied. The purpose is to form an overall first impression and to detect mannerisms such as preferentially resting or pointing one leg, which could indicate soreness. This is also a time to check for symmetry from right to left by observing the horse from as many different angles as possible. As soon as the horse is caught, look him over from front, back, and either side before moving in for the detailed examination.

Eyes, Ears and Mouth

The examination should begin with the head. Teeth merit special attention in the older horse. It is normal for the upper teeth to overlap the lower ones both in front and on the sides; however, a dramatic overbite of the incisors (called a parrot mouth) should be avoided. Broken teeth are prone to infection, and missing teeth may affect chewing. The outer edges of the upper back teeth and lingual (toward the tongue) side of the lower arcade should checked for sharp edges or points that form when the teeth are not regularly filed (floated). Finally, the last cheek teeth should be examined for large sharp hooks that form when floating is not done properly. (This is an extremely common problem as reaching these teeth is very difficult in most horses.) The mouth in general should be pink, moist and free of unpleasant odors or breaks in the mucus membrane.

Nasal passages should be wide and free of any white or yellow discharge. You should be able to see the glistening of the mucus membranes inside the nose without moving the upper part of the nostril out of the way. The veterinarian will examine these areas carefully, as well as the sinuses, for normal conformation and signs of tumor or infection.

The horse should hold his eyes widely open, and they should be free of discharge or white color in the cornea (indicating a scar). The pupils should react by becoming smaller in bright light. Although complete examination requires an ophthalmoscope, much useful information can be gained by observing behavioral clues such as reluctance to move from bright to dark areas or shying, which could indicate visual problems.

Hearing can be checked by rattling a feed tub when the horse is not looking or making a sharp noise outside the stall. Also, the base of the ears should be checked for tumors or cysts.

The Respiratory System

A thorough examination of the chest and upper respiratory tract also requires a veterinarian, but a prospective buyer can make many helpful appraisals. The area between the jaws at the top of the neck contains the larynx and throat. It should be wide enough to admit a medium orange. The trachea, or windpipe, lies along the midline of the neck, feels very rigid and has ridges like a vacuum-cleaner hose—the tracheal cartilages. At the top of the neck it is possible to partially encircle the trachea and apply finger pressure along its sides. If it feels mushy and compresses easily, or if pressure produces a cough, irritation is present. The respiratory rate at rest is normally eight to twelve breaths per minute. The chest should move equally on both sides and respiration should appear effortless. Horses with chronic lung disease may show a double effort and a prominent use of the muscles along and behind the arch of the ribs when they exhale. This is called a heave line and indicates trouble moving air.

During and after exercise, the horse should be watched for any unusual noises, discharge or difficulty out of proportion to the work. The veterinarian will also check the lungs at this critical stage and, if indicated, may examine the throat and larynx with an endoscope—a long, flexible tube with a light source that is passed through the nostril.

General Condition of the Horse

The skin, coat and general condition of a horse are nonspecific indicators of disease and health. With an older horse, pay particular attention to any lumps or growths. This is especially important with gray horses, which commonly develop tumors called melanomas in their later years. Melanomas usually begin in the anal area and along the undersurface of the tail and are thus easily overlooked. Your veterinarian can check for internal spread with a rectal examination. You should also be wary of a horse that does not shed out properly or on time as this may be a sign of a pituitary tumor in the brain, another problem associated with age.

You can tell a great deal about how the gastrointestinal tract is functioning by the horse's general condition, appetite and amount and quality of manure. In addition to listening to the abdomen with a stethoscope, the veterinarian should perform a rectal examination to evaluate the condition of the intestinal arteries (often severely damaged by a lifetime's exposure to parasites) and to check for other abnormalities such as tumors or abscesses. With the latter, even a rectal exam may fail to detect the problem if the mass lies far to the front of the abdomen or down along the lower abdominal wall. (Note: The seller may rightfully not wish a rectal to be performed as there is always a risk the rectum could be perforated. While the chances of this happening are extremely small, the result can be disastrous. Also, the veterinarian may wish to have special accommodations for restraint in the case of a rectal examination. For these reasons, it is wise to discuss this matter with both parties before the time of the prepurchase examination.)

The Musculoskeletal System

The area of primary concern to everyone is the musculoskeletal system. Always begin by comparing the muscles on either side. Any asymmetry could indicate pain in the leg has resulted in decreased use and concomitant loss of muscle bulk and strength on the affected side. Loss of muscle evenly over the hindquarters may also signal a chronic problem with tying-up or altered blood supply. Palpate the muscles along the spine and croup for signs of spasm and tenderness that usually correlate with a hock or stifle lameness. (Note: This last examination should be done with extreme caution. The horse will often stand quietly while you palpate his back until a single point of tenderness is reached. The speed and ferocity of his reaction to pressure there may take you completely off guard.)

Proceeding to the legs, there should be good muscling above the knee and hock. The lower legs should be as close to a perfectly straight support as possible, and a line perpendicular to the ground should travel directly through the center of the knee, cannon bone, footlock joint and point of the toe. Deviations result in concussive and compressive forces being concentrated in the deviated area rather than traveling directly through to the foot. This is a defect at any age, but even minor problems are compounded in time. It is particularly important in an older horse, especially if his trimming has attempted to eliminate any abnormal gait (e.g., paddling).

If there is crookedness to a leg, particular attention should be paid to those joints where the deviation occurs. A common fault is toes pointing outward from the fetlock down. This places strain on the inside of the fetlock joint, which must bear the weight without benefit of support from the pastern and foot. Such horses will paddle (swing the leg to the inside or outside) when they move. This depends usually on whether they are base wide or base narrow (feet positioned inside or outside of a line drawn down from where the legs leave the chest). This often leads to corrective shoeing and trimming that eliminates the paddling but makes the strain worse. When the foot is trimmed to bring the breakover point of the toe back under the knee, instead of in line with the pastern, a further break in the straight line through the bones to the ground is added at the coffin joint level. Ringbone may result, as well as sidebone formation and formation of navicular bone spurs on one side.

If you spot any deviation from normal in the axis of the leg, inspect the involved joints carefully for heat or swelling. Equally significant is a decrease in joint fluid (your veterinarian will check for

Prospective horse buyers may be on the lookout for the narrow heels and shrunken frogs that are associated with navicular disease.

signs of this). It may be advisable to X-ray such joints before purchasing the horse (more on X-rays follows).

The technique of pinpointing potential problem areas by drawing a line through the leg to the ground is a simple one. Once you master the technique, you will be amazed at how much easier it becomes to zero in on a lameness. For best results, stand the horse squarely on level ground and take a photograph from directly in front and directly behind. You can then examine these at your leisure, using a ruler or straight edge. When able, X-rays are even more helpful in studying the alignment of the bones and the appearance of unilateral bony changes, such as navicular spurs or sidebone. They can also provide clues as to how long and how severely the conformation and/or trimming has been stressing the legs.

The next step is to actually run your hands down every inch of the legs. There are four major things to look for:

1. Heat

2. Swelling

3. Tenderness

4. Asymmetry

Of these, asymmetry is the easiest to detect and the most revealing. Even a relatively inexperienced examiner can notice a difference in two legs. The veterinarian will make a more detailed examination, including the inspection above, evaluation of range of movement and flexion tests.

Always pay special attention to the feet. An obvious change in angulation from the pastern bone to the hoof, when viewed from the side, may indicate old founder or fracture. Rings on the hooves indicate founder, change in nutritional status or a severe disease like pneumonia with high fever. The heels are very important. Narrow heels and a shrunken frog correlate with navicular disease or any painful problem in the foot. (An exception would be for Saddlebreds that wear an artificial foot and do not normally have direct pressure on their soles. They may show some atrophy of the frog and/or narrowing at the heels.) Uneven heels reveal the horse is landing harder on the side with the higher heel, either because of pain on the other side of the foot or because of improper trimming. Finally, if the horse is shed with anything other than a plain, flat shoe, get an explanation.

The Horse in Motion

Evaluating a horse in motion requires considerable experience. The veterinarian will be of much help here. Your opinion of how attractively a horse moves may very well be important to the decision of whether or not to buy the horse but does not necessarily relate to his actual soundness. There is one way of detecting even subtle lamenesses and/or gait imbalances that can be mastered by anyone and uses a sense you would not normally rely upon—your hearing.

The better your sense of rhythm and concentration, the easier it will be to learn this. Simply listen to the horse walking and jogging slowly on a hard surface (concrete barn aisles are perfect). If you focus on the cadence of his steps, any interruption to the smooth, almost hypnotically even footfall of a sound, balanced horse will be immediately obvious. Listen first with your eyes closed or back turned and then look and listen together to identify the offending limb. You will probably be more sensitive, at least initially, to a louder footfall. This will be associated with the good leg as it takes more weight and lands more heavily. Identify the loud leg and look for trouble in the opposite leg. The problem could also be located in the leg that has just given up support. For example, if the right front lands hard, check the left front and left hind.

A sensitive rider can also learn a great deal from the horse's back, particularly about the hindquarters. Any reluctance to assume either lead or a marked difference in the feel of a posting trot to either side should be reported to the veterinarian. Most horses (and riders) have a stronger side, which does not necessarily mean they are lame on the other. However, this conformation may back up a subtle impression of trouble the veterinarian had from the ground.

X-rays

The final stage in a veterinarian's examination is the taking of X-rays. Opinions are as widely separated on this subject as they are on the need of the examination in general. There are those who maintain X-rays are so difficult to interpret they are virtually useless, while others place such stock in them they drift from horse to horse in quest of the perfect set of X-rays.

In many ways, the nays have it in this argument, but only because most people's expectations extend well beyond the information any X-rays can provide.

The basic data an X-ray offers is whether an area looks normal or not. It cannot tell you if the lesion is currently, or will in the future be, causing pain. There are horses around with fetlocks that are such a mass of extra calcium deposition that the joint is almost unrecognizable, or with sidebone calcification that looks on X-rays like a set of antlers, but the horse is without pain. There are also those with early pathology in the soft tissues, such as navicular or cunean (hock) bursitis, that are terribly lame but appear normal on an X-ray.

A solid approach is to at least take X-rays of the feet. The old saying "No foot, no horse" is all too true. It is also a fact that 60% to 90% of all lamenesses can be traced to the foot. You are also more likely to pick up one of the few absolute reasons to turn down a horse, such as early low (involving the joint) ringbone.

The lesson here is not to abandon X-rays, but to use them in conjunction with all the other information from the history and physical examination.

Other Tests

In addition to the physical examination and any X-rays, the veterinarian may suggest any number of blood tests in addition to the normal Coggins. This would be unusual, though, unless some specific problem was suspected. It is wise to have the veterinarian store a blood sample for drug analysis in the event the horse goes lame or has a dramatic personality change soon after purchase.

This step can protect both buyer and seller from a round of recriminations over who did what to the horse and when. Such sampling is not routinely done and the seller may initially take offense at the suggestion. Since there is really no reason to object, tactfully point out the benefits while making it clear that such sampling is a condition of sale. A seller who refuses to comply must certainly be considered suspect.

As a practical note, it is advisable to inform the seller that you will require blood for possible drug testing well in advance of your veterinarian's arrival. I recall once performing an exhaustive examination with full X-rays from knee and hock down only to have the seller's jaw drop to the floor at the mention of drug testing. They packed up the horse and swept him off in a cloud of protest and indignation, leaving the potential buyer with a sizable bill that probably could have been avoided. Since there is nothing to be gained by surprising people with this testing, give them the chance to refuse before wasting your time and money on an examination.

Making a Decision

At the conclusion of all this testing, the veterinarian will be able to tell you two things. First, if there are any pathological changes in the legs, lungs and other parts of the horse, and second, if they are causing the horse a problem at the time of the examination, that is, if he is lame, short of breath and so forth. It is entirely possible for a lesion or disease to be present but not be causing symptoms at the time of the examination, much as you might have an old injury that only aches in certain weather or with certain activities. According to the guidelines of the American Association of Equine Practitioners, the veterinarian should not pass or fail the horse, and he or she will not be able to tell you if any given abnormal finding will eventually cause a problem. To do either of these things is beyond the scope of a veterinarian's responsibility.

While the buyer must make the ultimate decision on purchase, the veterinarian can help by supplying some details of the condition(s).

For example, take the common situation where an older horse's X-ray examination reveals changes in the navicular bone. The veterinarian, or a consulting radiology expert, will be able to tell you if the degree of change falls within the normal pattern for a horse of that age. This opinion may be further modified if you know the horse's history involving excessive stress (e.g., racing). The X-rays may also indicate if the process is old and slow versus new and active. Add whether or not the horse was moving soundly or had contracted narrow heels or special shoeing, and the possible significance of the X-ray changes becomes more clear.

The veterinarian can also tell you how the activity level you desire of the horse influences the course of navicular disease in general.

CHAPTER THIRTEEN

THE CHANGING ROLE OF ALTERNATIVE AND COMPLEMENTARY MEDICINE

In the introduction to this book we described how medical care is changing with a shift toward preventative medicine and research into age-related degenerative diseases. When you go to the family doctor today, you are likely to be asked how things are at home, if you wear your seat belt, if you are keeping to a healthful diet, etc.—even if the reason for your visit was a stubbed toe. The emphasis is shifting from care for a disease or disorder to care for the whole person, as physicians realize the function of all organ systems is intertwined.

An increasing number of vets agree with the philosophy that it makes sense to take care of the whole animal rather than focus on the part that's ailing.

It certainly makes sense to take care of a whole person or animal rather than focusing just on a part that is ailing. The total care concept, "people are more than just a sum of their parts," is the cornerstone of osteopathic medicine (the doctors with the D.O. degree instead of M.D.) and what is today called a holistic approach (shortened from wholistic). We don't have a veterinary equivalent of D.O.s, but the holistic approach is growing by leaps and bounds, for horses and other animals as well. These once fringe element medicines do not abandon drugs and surgery, but they do try to avoid them by preventing problems serious enough to require them. If a serious problem does occur, treatment does not stop at the drug or surgery needed to solve it. Treatment extends to investigating how the system broke down in the first place and how it can be strengthened to prevent future problems.

The inroads in equine care are not as obvious yet as they are in human medicine. Veterinarians still don't concentrate on diet as much as they should, and you may not be interrogated about the last time you had your horse's teeth floated or his feet trimmed every time you call the vet.

Acupuncture, massage and even chiropractic treatments—unheard of 20 years ago—are widely available. Alternative therapy devices such as magnetic therapy and laser treatments are advertised everywhere. There is a rapidly growing interest in herbs and nutrition as alternatives to traditional medications. People involved with horses at all levels and in all different sports are trying these alternatives. It is no longer only the oddballs. The effort is very unfocused right now—we don't have enough veterinarians who can look at a horse and be familiar with all the possible therapy alternatives to determine what might work best and be best for the horse in the long run. Does he need a couple days' worth of bute pills or icing and magnetic therapy or massage and chiropractic care or a decent blacksmith to straighten out his feet—all or none of the above?

As is true of anything, there are strengths and weaknesses to these various alternatives to traditional medicine and traditional treatments. Acupuncture is not the answer to everything any more than drugs are—or chiropractic care or nutritional approaches, herbal remedies, etc. People are experimenting with different approaches because they are dissatisfied with allopathic medicine. Bute works well until you stop giving it. Both veterinarians and owners tend to forget the drug was never intended to be a cure. There was a very large piece of the treatment puzzle missing—the part that actually fixes what was wrong in the first place or at least gives a long-term plan to arrest the problem, make the horse more comfortable or even reverse some of the damage. No single discipline is all good or all bad; none has all the answers and none is the best. The challenge is to critically examine what each discipline has to offer, keep what is valid and discard the nonsense.

We need to keep the idea that the best approach to health is building the healthiest possible horse to begin with, one whose bones, muscles and joints are able to withstand the stresses they encounter; one whose immune system is strong and able to fight off the infections that challenge him every day. We do not do that by

The best approach to health is building the healthiest possible horse to begin with.

giving drugs. Drugs are designed for diseases. A whole horse approach that concentrates on making the animal as resistant to disease and injury as possible will automatically eliminate the need for many drugs. On the other hand, a rabid anti-drug attitude is not good either.

We will probably never eliminate disease. Even if we learned enough about the internal workings of the horse's body and knew how to make every cell function at its maximum efficiency, there would still be the outside world to deal with. Viruses; bacteria; other organisms; chemicals making their way in through the skin, the intestinal tract, and the lungs; physical forces; trauma and injury—all of these things can at least temporarily throw even the perfect system off base. This is where drugs come in. There will always be times when the horse's system has something go wrong, and correcting it as quickly as possible is the best thing to do. Disease can be likened to a house on fire. Before the fire the house was perfect and functional. When the fire started, sections were being rapidly destroyed. The only way to stop it was to bury the house in a deluge of water and fire-fighting chemicals. The fire was treated/put out but what is left? Remember that drugs come with price tags in terms of side effects, their benefits disappear as soon as the drug clears the horse's system and all drugs are to some extent poisons. When drugs are needed, a simultaneous search for any weaknesses in the horse's health that led him to develop the problem in the first place should be made and corrective measures taken. If that burning house had a sprinkler system (maximal health), the fire could have been put out with minimal damage. It is much easier to replace a ruined trashcan and a few feet of tile or carpet surrounding it than the whole house. If disease control mechanisms in the horse's body are functioning properly, he can put out all those little fires before they spread into a serious disease. What makes more sense—to treat a horse with chronic skin infections endlessly with medicated shampoos and antibiotic shots or to correct the deficiencies or toxicities that weakened his defense to those skin infections so that he stops getting them?

CHAPTER FOURTEEN

MANAGEMENT OF THE OLDER BROODMARE AND STALLION

A broodmare's useful reproductive life should extend well into her teens; in some cases even into the early 20s. However, each pregnancy takes its toll on the physical structures and age itself gradually results in dropping levels of sex hormones. Low-grade uterine infections may cause a degree of scarring that will eventually interfere with successful pregnancy.

Physical Changes

Gravity is one force we cannot avoid. Multiple pregnancies cause stretching of the muscles and ligaments of the abdominal wall and the ligaments which support the uterus. The constant tug and pull may be one reason why older broodmares develop conformational changes in the vaginal area. Because of stretching, pregnancy may be more uncomfortable for the older mare. She would show this by not moving around as much and often appearing colicky. However, it is not all that unusual to find mares who have sailed through 12 or more pregnancies.

The primary reason for mentioning these potential physical changes in older mares is to suggest a little empathy is in order. Be alert to signs the mare may be significantly slowed down or uncomfortable from the pregnancy. She may not be a very good candidate for turn out with a large group of mares where the younger ones may successfully compete for her food. Her ability to defend herself and her social standing in the group are likely to drop. Maintaining the mare's body condition during pregnancy is important to guaranteeing adequate nutrients are getting to the foal. If an older mare shows signs of weight loss, recognize that discomfort and competition may be keeping her from getting adequate food and make arrangements for special care. A smaller group or even her own stall and paddock will relieve some of the pressures, allow her to get undisturbed rest and make it possible to monitor her feed intake and ensure she eats enough.

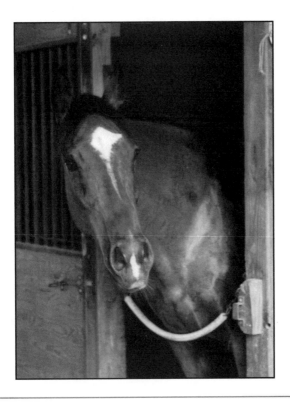

A pregnant older horse may not be a good candidate for turn out with a large group of mares, where she may not be able to defend herself or get enough to eat.

Uterine Infections

Uterine infections are a common problem in all farm animals. As a mare ages, the ligaments supporting the external genitalia weaken. The vaginal area then begins to tilt inward (versus the normal vertical position), making air sucking and fecal contamination more likely. Infections may be severe, with an obviously abnormal dis-

251

charge and fever, or relatively mild, with the mare showing no obvious clinical signs except for some difficulty in getting back in foal or in staying in foal. Uterine infections always result in some degree of scarring of the wall of the uterus. Even the effects of mild infections will add up over time, and the end result may be a uterus that does not have sufficient normal area to support the placenta. Such problems are likely as the placenta normally attaches over a larger percentage of the surface area of the uterus. There is very little uterine lining not involved in the support of a pregnancy.

The usual problem seen with uterine scarring is early abortion. The mare may seem to have conceived (e.g., failed to come back into heat and had rectal examinations compatible with pregnancy) but is found to be open (not pregnant) on the routine 45-day examination. Most of these mares do get pregnant, but abnormalities in the uterus prevent the placenta from developing normally and the pregnancy is lost.

Diagnosis of uterine scarring is made by removing a small piece of the uterus with a special biopsy instrument and submitting it for microscopic examination. This is a relatively simple procedure and can be performed on most mares without any need for sedatives or anesthesia. The procedure has been around for quite some time, and experienced pathologists can very accurately predict the general condition of the whole uterus from just this tiny sample. The chances of keeping a mare with uterine scarring in foal are directly related to how severe the changes are and also to the presence or absence of any other problems. While it is true that even mares who would be considered sterile based on their biopsy results have managed to carry a foal, the chances are extremely slim. The accuracy of reproductive predictions based on uterine biopsies is generally so high that this is probably the single most informative and important test to be done with aged mares experiencing breeding problems.

Mares should also be tested for active uterine infections by culturing a sample of the fluid in the uterus. Even before the scarring develops, active infections may prevent conception by causing swelling of the tissues. Changes in the fluids of the reproductive tract interfere with the sperm and egg. Even if fertilization of the egg does occur, the egg may be unable to attach to the inflamed uterine wall and will die within a matter of days.

Culture of the uterus is a very simple procedure. A long, sterile culture tube is carefully passed through the cervix and into the uterus. Once the tube is situated, a sterile cotton swab is pushed through it and allowed to absorb the materials to be cultured. It is then withdrawn safely inside the tube and removed. Again, sedation and/or anesthesia are usually not required.

When infection is found, the organism should always be tested to see which antibiotics would be most effective. This is done by growing the organism on a culture plate together with several small paper discs that are impregnated with various antibiotics. If the organism is sensitive to one or more of the drugs, it will fail to grow in the area surrounding that particular disc. This is called sensitivity testing.

Once the appropriate drug is located, the mare is treated by instillation of a solution containing that antibiotic directly into the uterus. This is done daily for approximately four to 10 days, depending on the severity of infection. It is sometimes possible to place a piece of tubing inside the uterus. The tubing is sutured to the skin of the vulva so that owners may do the daily infusions themselves, thus cutting some costs. This technique is not suitable for all mares as the tubes can become easily dislodged if the mare rubs the area or if she pulls away during the infusion.

If a severe infection is present, it may also be necessary to stimulate the uterus to contract in hopes of causing it to force out some of the infected materials. In these cases, the veterinarian will administer the drug Pitocin and possibly estrogens.

When treating uterine infections, it must always be remembered that clearing the infection is only part of the battle. The final result will also depend on how extensive the scarring changes are. Since time is of the essence when treating an aged mare, it may be advisable to have a uterine biopsy performed before even deciding to treat an infection. There may already be a significant amount of uterine scarring present.

Uterine infections result from a number of contributing factors. Many infections are acquired at foaling when the conditions within the uterus are very favorable for bacterial growth. There is certainly no way to render the foaling conditions sterile within a barn, but it is important to minimize gross contamination of the mare during this time. This is the reason behind wrapping the tail and keeping the vaginal area free of caked dirt or secretions before foaling, picking out the foaling stall regularly, using disinfectants on foaling stall walls and floors and cleaning up the mare as soon as possible after foaling. Such measures are not 100% effective, but may help keep contamination to a level the mare can handle without becoming infected. It is also common practice on many large breeding farms to flush out the mare's uterus with saline solution soon after foaling. This helps clear out the debris bacteria needs to grow and also stimulates the uterus.

Mares may also develop reproductive-tract infections at other times as a result of poor conformation. In a normal mare, the vaginal lips run roughly perpendicular to the ground. However, as a result of hereditary poor conformation or aging, many mares show a tipping of the vagina that gives them an inward slant or caved-in appearance at the vagina. The seal of the vaginal lips is not very effective in such mares, with the result that air and fecal material may enter the vagina. In addition, the opening of the urinary tract—the urethra—is located inside the vagina. Mares with the abnormal conformation often have a problem with some urine running back toward the uterus instead of to the outside. Termed urine pooling, this also increases the likelihood of infection and/or inflammation.

There are surgical procedures to correct these problems. The simplest is a Caslick's operation. This involves suturing shut the top portion of the vagina and leaving just enough of an opening to allow urination. It is very effective in preventing air and other materials from entering the vagina. A Caslick's will not correct urine pooling and a more complicated plastic surgery to reposition the urethra is needed in such mares.

These surgeries are performed with the mare standing and with the use of only a local or spinal anesthetic. As mentioned, they are usually quite effective. Before performing surgery on an aged mare it is always advisable to perform a uterine biopsy to determine the extent of any permanent damage and to culture the mare and clear any infections.

Pregnancy Loss

Aged mares have an overall 25% to 30% chance of early loss of the pregnancy, compared to about 10% for younger mares. Uterine scarring that decreases the area available for the placenta to implant is one cause. Another factor may be death of the fetus due to chromosomal defects, which are more common as the eggs age. All eggs are present from the time of the mare's birth.

Another problem that can cause early death of the fetus is insufficient production of the hormone progesterone. Progesterone is essential to the maintenance of a normal pregnancy. The causes for a low level in mares is not well understood; it may occur even in mares that appear perfectly normal. Once the problem is diagnosed (through testing for hormone levels in the blood), it may be possible to supplement the progesterone by intramuscular injections and save the pregnancy.

Hemorrhage of the Uterine Artery

In addition to the increased problems with getting and keeping an aged mare in foal, the higher risks of pregnancy itself must be considered.

Aged mares are more prone to suffering hemorrhage of the uterine artery during foaling. The uterine arteries are large vessels that provide the majority of the blood supply for the uterus. There are two, the left and right uterine arteries. They travel from the aorta to the uterus through a sheet of tissue that also serves to support the uterus. These arteries grow during pregnancy to meet the demands of the placenta. With time, the walls may become weakened and the artery may rupture during foaling.

Many mares survive their first episode of uterine artery rupture because the tissues around the vessel contain the bleeding until the local pressure becomes great enough to stop it. However, mares may die the first time this happens, and the risks of losing the mare rise sharply if she becomes pregnant and experiences a rupture again.

Clinical signs of uterine-artery rupture are those of shock. The mare becomes weak, trembles, and breaks out into a sweat. If the blood loss is large, she may go down and show a weak pulse, and if hemorrhage is not controlled by pressure from the surrounding tissues, she can die.

The latest vascular research in man and animals suggests that copper and magnesium status may be very important in preserving the health of the blood vessels.

257

The area of hemorrhage can be felt on rectal examination, and any mare known by such examination to have had a previous uterine-artery rupture should not be bred.

Pregnancy and Lameness

Pregnancy also carries other risks that, though not fatal, can seriously affect a mare's health. Of primary consideration is the effect of pregnancy on chronic lamenesses.

Many mares are first retired to breeding when they develop a lameness problem. While it is true that speed work and jumping create the greatest problems for most lamenesses, the increased weight of pregnancy can also place considerable stress on chronic lamenesses. This is most likely to be a problem with foot troubles or tendon and/or ligament injuries, although other joints may be affected as well. If the pregnancy causes increased pain from such problems, the mare will move around less and is likely not to eat or drink enough. This has an adverse effect on fetus and mother alike. Some veterinarians also believe that the large shifts in hormones associated with pregnancy can worsen some types of arthritis.

To minimize or eliminate lameness complications in the broodmare, the first step must be to establish that she has minimal or no pain or problems ambulating before she is even bred. Not enough is known about the possible effects of common analgesic drugs on the fetus, while other agents (the steroid family) could make the mare more likely to abort. Therefore, the lameness should be stable and trimming and/or shoeing procedures well established prior to breeding the mare.

During pregnancy, the caretaker and/or farm manager should be well aware of any previous lameness problems a mare has had so that she can be watched closely for any signs of trouble. If she does begin to show lameness she should be removed from any large groups and maintained where she will not have to compete for food and water or deal with aggressive pasturemates. Every effort should be made to relieve the pain by adjustments in trimming and shoeing together with massage, supportive legwraps, hydrotherapy, poultices and liniments rather than resorting immediately to drugs. When pain cannot be controlled by these measures and results in loss of condition, drug therapy will be necessary but should be kept to a minimum. With severe lamenesses, neurectomy (cutting the nerve supply to the area) or a long-term nerve block may be preferable to heavy use of systemic drugs. Alcohol blocks involve the injection of strong alcohol solutions around the nerve and last for several months.

Broodmare Nutrition

The other major pregnancy-related problems are those related to nutrition. These include generalized loss of condition, anemia and bone problems.

As the horse ages, there may be a decreased efficiency of the digestive tract. This becomes a significant problem when the mare must deal with the other demands specific to pregnancy—i.e., greater need for total calories but increasing abdominal distention that causes discomfort and often decreased appetite. The diet of the aged pregnant mare should be very carefully planned to maximize the calorie content of the feeds while still keeping sufficient fiber to aid normal digestion. This is covered in detail in Chapter Three, "The Basic Diet."

The breeding season and lactation period also have specific caloric requirements. It is a common myth (or half-truth) that fat mares are harder to get in foal. The fact is that research has shown that animals that are on a rising plane of nutrition are the easiest to breed. A rising plane of nutrition refers to a high-quality diet and a gradual weight gain. Very fat or very thin mares are both more difficult to breed. Therefore, nutritional planning for the broodmare should begin before she is even taken to the breeding shed.

Many vitamins and minerals play critical roles in fertility. Vitamin A/carotene supplements are widely used in late winter in mares scheduled to be bred that spring (grazing on lush spring pastures is nature's way of getting this vitamin into the mare before breeding season). You can use one of the synthetic supplements or get the same effect by adding a few pounds of quality alfalfa hay and a few pounds of carrots to her daily diet. The trace minerals zinc and selenium also influence fertility. Liberal allowances should be made for these minerals. They are not only commonly borderline to deficient in most diets but the mare's age dictates good supplementation. So do the needs of the foal she will be carrying. The best way to bring the mare into nutritional fitness for breeding is to feed a high-quality hay, preferably with some alfalfa, free choice as well as a supplement containing the B vitamins, vitamin C, vitamin E and all trace minerals, providing zinc at a level of 100 to 150 mg/day, copper about 50 mg/day and at least two mg/day of supplemental selenium. Flaxseed meal or oil are also beneficial, and I have also had some success using gamma oryzanol supplement (Body Builder™) for mares that show weak estrus periods.

If the mare has been getting the usual subsistence diet of barren mare hay (a euphemism for the worst possible hay), she will require several weeks of a good diet before she is likely to conceive. The feed chosen should be the same that will be used throughout pregnancy and lactation. The mare should be gradually brought up to the level it is anticipated she will need for the first half of pregnancy. A slow weight gain is desirable at this time. Even in the early parts of pregnancy it can be expected that the aged mare will develop problems during her pregnancy that prevent adequate intake of calories. A small weight gain early on acts as an insurance policy against her losing too much condition. While extreme obesity should be avoided early in the breeding season and pregnancy, calorie-counting has absolutely no place in the management of the aged broodmare.

Finally, during lactation, the calorie requirements are about twice what they are for the breeding season and first half to two-thirds of the pregnancy. If the mare had problems during the pregnancy, she may have lost a considerable amount of condition, placing her in a yet more precarious position. It is best to plan increases in feed so that the mare is being offered the amount of feed required to maintain lactation by the time she reaches the last three to four weeks of pregnancy. She probably won't always eat this much, but by keeping her ahead of anticipated calorie needs you should avoid having to catch up after foaling when you discover the mare is in poor condition.

In addition to the need for increased calories to nourish herself and the growing foal, the mare requires additional vitamins and minerals. The greatest demands are placed on B vitamins, calcium, phosphorus, copper and iron—the key elements in forming blood (prevention of anemia) and in forming and maintaining normal bones and teeth.

During pregnancy, the blood volume increases and the mare will need to manufacture more red blood cells. She must also supply all the elements that the developing foal needs to make his own red blood cells. This places a large drain on the stores of iron in the body and calls for adequate amounts of B-12, folate (another B vitamin), and copper. The pregnant mare's diet will usually contain adequate amounts of these elements or, in the case of the B vitamins, adequate nutrition so that the intestine's microorganisms can manufacture them. For this system to operate smoothly, the mare must eat regularly and well and have a perfectly normal digestive tract. Since repeated pregnancies drain iron stores, it may be possible that an aged mare could still become anemic with a good diet and healthy appetite. However, do not routinely give high iron supplements. These can be very toxic. First confirm that she needs iron.

The best course is to have the mare's hemoglobin and hematocrit checked prior to breeding or in early pregnancy and again in the last trimester. The testing need only be a hematocrit to measure the percentage of red blood cells in the blood and a hemoglobin level to measure the amount of iron in the red blood cells. These tests are fairly inexpensive. They can tell you if the mare is anemic and also help determine what elements she is lacking. If anemia is detected, further tests may be recommended to pinpoint the exact deficiency. Supplementation may then be given in the feed or by injection. Don't immediately think "iron" when you hear low blood counts. There are many possible causes and iron won't help most of them.

Calcium and phosphorus are probably the most neglected components of a pregnant mare's diet, yet deficiencies of these elements result in bone and joint deformities in the foal and weakening of the bones and joints of the mare (osteoporosis). In a retrospective study of metabolic bone disease (osteochondrosis dessicans) in foals, it was found that farms with the lowest incidence fed a diet containing 1.2% calcium. The greatest incidence was found on a farm feeding 0.2% calcium diets, indicating a direct link between calcium intake and the incidence of metabolic bone disease in foals. In the mare, a deficiency in the diet results in her body trying to make up the difference by dissolving her bones to provide the needed calcium and phosphorus for the foal. With each pregnancy she loses more and more bone until joints begin to lose their support. Fractures appear virtually anywhere—most commonly in areas already weakened by an arthritic process, such as the navicular bone.

The newest information regarding pregnancy and nutrition relates to the roles of zinc and copper in preventing metabolic bone disease. The same study recommends that levels of 90 mg/kg of zinc be fed during pregnancy to decrease the chances of metabolic bone disease. This is greater than twice what the current NRC (National Research Council) suggests. Given that zinc is well tolerated at levels of up to even 500 mg/kg/day and that older horses have decreased efficiency of absorption, I would recommend feeding the higher level of zinc to a pregnant mare. A supplemental source of zinc will be required. Consult your veterinarian or an equine nutritionist for advice.

With copper, the recommended level to prevent metabolic bone disease (30 to 50 mg/kg) is three to five times that listed as appropriate in the NRC guidelines. Again, however, the higher level is safe. Older mares commonly have low serum levels of copper and that low serum copper is believed to be associated with another problem of pregnancy, ruptured ovarian artery. For these reasons, I recommend supplementing mares up to the higher level of copper intake. The other trace minerals (selenium, iodine, manganese) are also critical to the health of the mare and foal.

To obtain the best possible outcome, all nutrients need to be present in the pregnant mare's diet in levels adequate both for her and the very rapidly growing foal. Foals born weak, small or crooked legged are largely the result of suboptimal nutrition.

Nutrition has traditionally been focused on the last part of pregnancy, but nutrition is important from the day the mare conceives. Commercially available pregnant mare feeds usually contain too many calories for the first half or so of pregnancy. For the first five or six months, feed the mare the same high-quality diet recommended for all older horses (see Chapter Three). When her need for calories starts to go up, as judged by a decrease in body fat, gradually switch her over to a pregnant mare feed.

The simplest, most effective, and in the end, most economical way to feed a pregnant mare during the last trimester is to use a high-quality, name brand commercial feed designed for pregnant mares, lactating (milking) mares and growing horses/weanlings. All three classes have roughly the same nutritional requirements.

Buying a Broodmare at Auction

Many broodmares are sold at auction where the information available is sketchy at best, and you will not have the benefit of a complete examination. In these cases, try to read between the lines of a mare's breeding history.

There are many possible reasons why a mare would fail to conceive in any given year. These would include postpartum infection or foaling trauma on the mare's side but also improper timing of breedings or poor semen quality—causes that have nothing to do with her fertility. I cannot give hard and fast guidelines here, but a rule of thumb would be that even a normal mare could have a failure rate of 10% to 25% (i.e., barren an average of one to two and one-half years out of 10, assuming she was bred every year).

However, you should check the foaling dates. A trend to steadily later foaling dates, leading up to a barren year, could indicate that the mare is difficult to breed and/or prone to infections that must be treated before she can be bred back. That is, if she consistently needs two or more cycles to conceive, foalings will get progressively later until she must miss a year. Also, caution is always advisable if the mare previously had a 100% conception rate but failed to conceive for one or more years immediately prior to her sale. While it may be that the present owner is unwilling to invest another season of maintenance in an aged mare, it may indicate that she has developed a problem. Owners are aware that this looks bad in a sales catalog and may try to explain somewhat in an Owner's Statement at the bottom of the page.

Many sales catalogs do not specify if a mare was bred or not in any year she failed to conceive. A listing of open means only that she was not carrying a foal, not that she was not bred. Barren usually means that she was bred but did not conceive or lost the foal early in the pregnancy. The use of the term is by no means universal and this listing may also mean that she was not bred. Always attempt to get a definition of the terminology used from the sales company.

You will want to evaluate a mare's breeding record in two ways. First, look at her lifetime breeding history. She should fall within the 10% to 25% failure rate for all the years she was actually bred. If you cannot determine whether or not she was bred any given year, check the foaling date from the preceding year. If it was early and her only use was as a broodmare, you must assume she was bred but did not conceive (or lost the foal) until proven otherwise. If her failure rate was above 25%, a clustering of the open or barren years probably represents some fertility problem at that time.

The second step is to evaluate the recent reproductive history, that is, the last four years. Ideally, you want a mare that had a foal the preceding year and is in foal at the time of the sale. Failing this, look for a mare who foaled the preceding year and is not bred back but has an owner's statement explaining why. If there is no owner's statement, there may be a recent problem that prompted this sale. This purchase would be a gamble; however, the foaling the previous year and recent onset of difficulty may mean it is something you can deal with successfully. If the mare did not have a foal the preceding year, the likelihood of there being a serious problem is higher and increases with each additional preceding year she did not foal. This is particularly true if her reproductive history prior to the last four years was normal.

If it cannot be determined whether or not she was bred, you probably should not buy this mare. However, if the history shows that she did conceive but lost the foal early in the pregnancy there is at least a chance that the problem may be treatable. Such early losses may be related to infection secondary to poor conformation (amenable to surgery) or to placental or uterine abnormalities that respond to progesterone injections during the critical months. However, they could also be related to uterine scarring that will not respond to any measures. The purchase would be a gamble but perhaps one well worth taking if the price is right. There is no reason to typecast these ladies. If the mare is otherwise healthy and sound, there is no reason why she could not change careers and be resold (or kept) as a riding or driving horse after some retraining.

To summarize, mares can produce foals well into their teens. Their experience in raising foals, known reproductive history and often reasonable price makes such mares a good choice for the first-time breeder, and many mares can also double as a family horse. Increasing age does result in an increased risk of fertility problems, greater number of risks associated with pregnancy and special nutritional requirements. Fortunately, modern veterinary medicine has much to offer in diagnosis and managing the special requirements of the aged broodmare. By working closely with your veterinarian, it is possible to maximize the reproductive efficiency and general health of the aged broodmare.

THE AGED BREEDING STALLION

Compared to mares, the breeding stallion has relatively few problems associated with age and/or time that refer specifically to his reproductive capacity. In fact, it is not at all unusual to hear of stallions performing quite adequately well into their 20s.

Breeding can be affected by nonspecific problems such as advancing arthritis, particularly if the disease involves extensive changes in the hindlegs and/or pelvis or spine that cause pain when the stallion must mount a mare. These studs may reach the point where they refuse to mount the mare and/or develop a syndrome of general poor condition and decreased sperm numbers or quality secondary to the stress of chronic pain.

Compared to mares, the older breeding stallion, such as this 22-year-old stallion, Cutter, has relatively fewer age-related problems.

Cardiovascular System Problems

Cardiovascular system problems involving the heart, its valves, or the major vessels appear with some degree of frequency in aged breeding stallions. This is probably primarily related to the fact that they commonly achieve such an advanced age and/or are allowed to live out their normal lifespans since they continue to perform a useful function. While these difficulties do not have any effect upon reproductive performance, it is advisable to remember that the likelihood of a significant circulatory problem increases with age and unusual exercise or stress should be avoided. One stress that cannot be controlled is the excitement of breeding. It is fairly common for such stallions to die during the act of breeding.

Declining Sperm Counts and Quality

Decline in sperm numbers and/or quality can be expected as a natural result of aging, but this rarely reaches the point where breeding must stop altogether. The sperm counts and quality should be checked by the veterinarian before the start of each breeding season and at intervals into the season so that the proper adjustments in bookings of mares can be planned. The magnitude of this problem is greatly reduced when the modern technology of semen extenders and methods for storing semen are employed.

Stallions who have learned bad habits such as biting and kicking should be re-educated so they can be safely exercised.

Declining Reproductive Efficiency

Declining reproductive efficiency is related to multiple changes in the endocrine balance. Injudicious use of male hormones is not advisable, nor is it likely to prove effective. In selected cases, it may be found that the problem is acutely linked to a drop in thyroid hormone levels, usually associated with a prolonged illness or serious injury. In these cases, the imbalance is caused by factors operating above and beyond those to be expected from aging, and the veterinarian may recommend a temporary and strictly monitored course of supplementation to aid recovery.

Managing the Aged Breeding Stallion

The key areas of management of the aged breeding stallion are exercise and diet. Reproductive activity does place a considerable stress on the cardiovascular system but does very little to maintain muscle tone and joint/tendon flexibility and strength. The naturally aggressive nature of stallions, together with special requirements for isolation, plus extremely strong and high fencing during turnout, often results in inadequate exercise. Stallions are naturally more exuberant, alert, playful, and strong than mares or geldings, but they are not naturally mean. It is important they be handled by someone who is comfortable with stallions. The handler should confine them to their stall to avoid confrontations or overreactions to their normal behavior with fear and excessive force.

271

A stallion who has been improperly handled and kept confined for a number of years can develop many dangerous vices such as biting, striking, kicking and charging any human in range. Even these patterns can be changed with proper handling. Every effort should be made to re-educate such horses so they can be safely exercised to maintain musculoskeletal fitness and to prevent any chronic arthritic problems from degenerating into permanent pain and stiffness.

Generally speaking, 15 to 20 minutes per day of free turnout, driving, longeing or riding is adequate for the breeding stallion. Heavier exercise schedules are not harmful (unless extremely stressful) as long as measures are made to provide dietary increases to meet the higher energy demands.

Most stallions are maintained at minimum exercise levels. Feeding them involves a very delicate balance of providing high-quality feed needed for top reproductive performance without causing excessive weight gain or digestive disturbances. The older breeding stallion should be fed exactly the same as any other older horse, realizing he may need additional calories (amount of grain and hay) to keep his weight during breeding season. Make sure he gets all the recommended levels of vitamins and minerals, as well as flaxseed oil or meal. Gamma oryzanol supplement has been reported to be beneficial for stallions as well.

CHAPTER FIFTEEN

TIPS FOR
SEASONAL CARE

Extremes of weather require certain management modifications for horses of any age. This is particularly important for the older horse. He is less adept at handling stress in general and may have some chronic problems that will aggravate and magnify those created by the weather.

WINTER

The winter months can be particularly hard on an older horse. The main problem to consider is infectious diseases. Cold weather and chills are not sufficient in and of themselves to cause any flu or sim-

The winter months can be hard on older horses. A horse that previously did not have to wear a blanket may have to wear one now.

ilar illness. However, these nonspecific stresses do lower the body's defenses against disease. As the horse ages, his natural immunity to infectious disease gradually declines anyway, making him a prime target in the winter for every infectious disease.

General preventative measures include limiting the horse's exposure to other horses, keeping him as warm and dry as possible, and making certain that his nutritional needs are adequately met.

274

Comfort

There is no need to actually quarantine the horse for the duration of the winter—and very little point to having him if you can't enjoy your normal activities. However, it certainly is wise to keep your horse away from other horses if you know he will be exposed to a disease and/or if the weather conditions are bad.

Keeping the horse as warm and dry as possible does not mean swaddling him in blankets and confining him to a stall. In order to tolerate the winter, he must be accustomed to the weather changes to some extent. What this recommendation refers to is common-sense measures such as not turning the horse out in bad weather unless he has a good shelter, providing him with a good all-weather blanket (such as a lined canvas turnout blanket), and drying him off immediately if he becomes wet. Barns need not be heated, and the horse will probably remain healthier if the difference between the barn and outside is not too great. An efficient system for exchanging the air should exist to avoid a build-up of stale and humid air, which can harbor large numbers of viruses or be heavy with irritating ammonia fumes or dust. Common sense is the best guide here, the goal being an airy barn that has no drafts directly hitting the horse.

Vaccinations

Since the older horse is more likely to come down with an infectious disease, it is wise to take particular care with his vaccination schedules (see Chapter Two, "Pinpointing the Preventable Causes of Aging"). We cannot fully protect the horse from infectious diseases with the vaccinations available, but they do afford some protection, and proper scheduling can maximize such coverage. Wintertime is the season for vaccination against rhinopneumonitis and influenza. Both are respiratory tract viruses, although rhinopneumonitis also causes abortion. The minimum recommended vaccination schedules for both diseases is once or possibly twice a year, depending upon the manufacturer. This minimum schedule is appropriate for horses who will probably not leave the farm during the winter and for those kept on a farm that has minimal or no traffic of horses on and off the premises, i.e., minimum exposure. Vaccinations should be given about two weeks before the time you would normally expect the most severe winter weather to begin. If your horse travels off the premises to show, hunt or perform any activity that exposes him to other horses, or if he is exposed to other horses on the premises, vaccination can be increased to as often as once per month to keep his antibody levels high. The schedule can be adjusted to accommodate periods of anticipated exposure during part of the winter, such as scheduling vaccinations two weeks to 10 days preceding an activity. The added cost of extra vaccinations is very minimal, when compared to having to treat respiratory infection for an extended period.

Feed

Meeting the nutritional demands of cold weather is important to maintaining the horse's resistance to disease. It also affects how he will cope with the other problems he may encounter in colder weather. The basic adjustment to be made in winter is the provision of more calories. The horse needs this extra energy just to keep up his body weight and will begin to burn fat to keep himself warm if underfed. To meet these cold weather needs, begin by increasing roughage, up to free choice hay. This not only provides the calories but actually generates heat within the body since hay is digested by fermentation in the large intestine and fermentation itself generates heat. If this fails, a good place to start might be to give 10% of the total feed ration required as grain. If the horse is already receiving grain, increase the total amount by 5% and make sure the hay you are using is the best quality available.

High-quality hay is not always readily available or may be very expensive in the winter. You can supplement the hay by using commercial mixed grass and alfalfa cubes (Montana Pride) or a small amount of pure alfalfa hay cubes (about two pounds a day)—if your horse's teeth are still good.

Another good calorie booster and special treat for the horse in winter is to provide a few pounds of a balanced hot mash (see recipe in Chapter Eleven, "Managing the Very Old Horse," page 208). The horse will easily tolerate $2^1/_2$ pounds of such a mash (half all the ingredient amounts) a few times a week, and it will provide added calories. If the horse still has difficulty holding his weight, try adding raw vegetable oil (see Chapters Three and Ten). Do not use store bought oils or the dry, prilled fat products that are animal lard.

Other, more general considerations related to feed include the needs to maintain a drinkable water source and to prevent grain and hay from becoming wet or frozen. The ideal is to have water available 24 hours a day and feed in perfect condition for as long as the horse cares to take to consume it. There may be times when it is impossible to meet this ideal, but any compromise invites colic or choke. If the horse has any tendency to show digestive problems, consider switching him to a management program that will minimize or avoid such problems as frozen water or feed. Hay of some sort should be available for most of the day. This may mean still feeding your good-quality hay in the appropriate amounts but buying a supply of lesser-quality plain grass hay (lesser-quality meaning later cutting; no sacrifices in terms of dirt or mold). You can offer lesser-quality hay between times when he is given his regular hay. Also, a great deal of hay is lost if the horse is fed outdoors in snow or mud. It may be necessary to feed as much as 25% to 50% more hay than you would to a horse confined to a stall just to keep him occupied and allow for losses. The horse that only gets hay and grain once or twice a day is more likely to chew the fences and fight at feeding time. Even more important, the digestive system is designed to accommodate almost constant eating. His stomach is relatively small and cannot tolerate a day's feed all at once. Feeding in this way can lead to overeating and colic and/or colic secondary to the abnormal eating pattern.

If electrolytes are added to the water, you should provide plain water, since a horse may not drink enough water with added electrolytes.

The best approach is to feed the grain in a minimum of two meals (the more the better) and keep hay available at all times. If a hay bunker or other way to keep the hay somewhat protected is available, you may wish to offer a good-quality mixed hay 24 hours a day. Alternately, you should hay the horse at least three times daily. Divide up the amount you calculate he would need if fed under more controlled circumstances and supplement this as necessary to allow for hay that is trampled or otherwise made inedible. The hay will keep the horse occupied and provide him with something in his digestive tract at all times.

Remember too that salt is just as important in the winter as in the summer. The horse will only need about $1^1/_2$ ounces a day but this is very important in maintaining his desire to drink enough water. Keep an eye on the salt block. If the horse is not using it, try offering free choice salt instead. Companies such as Buckeye Nutrition and Moorman's have various free salt formulas that are specifically made for horses. Do not use any salt that does not say it is for horses.

If you cannot locate a source of free choice salt, make sure you add $^1/_2$ to $^3/_4$ ounce of table salt to each of the horse's grain feedings.

Lameness and Foot Care

The other major problem that often is exacerbated in the winter is lameness. Frozen ground conditions frequently aggravate chronic problems, particularly foot problems. If the horse is being used less frequently, the chances are good he is not receiving the same routine attention from the blacksmith and owner, again leading to foot problems.

The horse should be given a thorough going over for signs of soreness prior to the worst part of winter. If necessary, your veterinarian should be called to define the problem and advise you on any necessary treatments or special precautions. This is particularly important for the horse that is turned out in a group. Feed often becomes a focal point of the group's day and fighting becomes more intense. The horse that is sore may be prevented from getting adequate food or water because he is too lame to compete.

Even previously sound horses can develop foot problems on frozen ground. This is particularly true if they were accustomed to wearing shoes but had them pulled for the winter. Generalized bruising and soreness is common under these conditions. You may also have trouble with more frequent abscesses and even thrush when the feet go unattended for long periods of time. Horses who remain shod may be less likely to have problems with bruising but can develop painful corns under their shoes if resetting schedules are not as frequent during the winter.

To prevent these problems, the horse's feet should be picked out daily if at all possible. He should also be observed at feeding times for any sign of lameness, including an apparent reluctance to join the group stampede at feeding time. The horse should be shod at the first sign of a shortened gait indicating foot tenderness. Rim or full pads should be used if simple shoeing alone is not enough to keep him comfortable. These problems are not likely to get better if shoeing is delayed, and they could lead to the horse not receiving proper nutrition.

Skin Care

Skin problems are another worry in the winter. Long winter coats often lead to moist, warm skin conditions underneath that are favorable to bacterial and fungal growths. This is exacerbated by exposing the horse to wet weather and by keeping him blanketed, with the most favorable conditions for skin infection occurring if he remains in a wet blanket. Also, the horse with a heavy winter coat will often be groomed less frequently, and those groomings will be less effective and complete. Once started, these skin infections, commonly known as rain rot, are notoriously difficult to clear up. The horse may show large, patchy, oozing bald areas in a surprisingly short period of time. The added nonspecific stress of the bad weather also makes him more likely to develop such infections and to show a decreased ability to control their spread.

The best treatment is prevention. There is no substitute for regular grooming. Heavy winter coats call for the regular and enthusiastic use of a curry comb and hard brush to lift out deep dirt and stimulate circulation. This can take hours, particularly if your grooming is sporadic, and a good investment is to buy a grooming vacuum that will make short work of deep dirt. If the horse is to be kept blanketed, he should have a good supply of sheets to wear underneath that can be washed easily when they become dirty or matted with hair. If he is on turnout, his outer blanket should be canvas to prevent his standing wet.

Unfortunately, even horses that are faithfully groomed may develop skin infections. If caught early, it is sometimes possible to clear them up with regular baths with an iodine-containing shampoo such as Betadine. Many cases remain resistant to this treatment as long as the winter coat is in place, with new areas of infection popping up just as you get on top of the last. In these circumstances, the best course is to clip the horse so that local treatment can be done readily. Clipping often uncovers disease that is far more widespread than you would first expect. Once a horse is clipped, most infections will respond to the iodine shampoo treatments within seven to 10 days. Resistant cases can usually be cleared by application of a final rinse containing the drug Captan, a common antifungal agent sold in nurseries and other garden supply stores. This is mixed at a rate of one tablespoon per gallon of water and applied to the horse; the excess is scraped off. The above course of treatment—clipping and bathing the affected areas daily with Betadine with or without Captan rinses—is strongly recommended for any horse who develops a skin infection on 10% or more of his body on first inspection. The older horse with decreased immunity is unlikely to respond to more conservative measures, and these infections are difficult to clear up under the best of circumstances.

SUMMER

Hot weather carries its own set of problems for the older horse. Dehydration and electrolyte disturbances head the list, with skin disease a close second.

Exercise

Most people have the sense not to overwork a horse in hot weather. Severe dehydration with electrolyte imbalance is blessedly rare when exercise is approached sensibly and the horse has free access to

When working an aged horse in hot weather, never exceed the limits of what he has been conditioned to do.

water and salt. The older horse may have hidden problems and weaknesses of his respiratory and cardiac systems that make overwork in hot weather particularly dangerous. It is essential to avoid any conditions that would interfere with the horse's normal intake of water and salt, even if the work he does is not extreme. A long day's showing or trail riding may not call for particularly hard and fast exercise, but the horse must go for long periods without feed, water or salt and may be forced to stand in a hot trailer for prolonged periods. Even a modest pace of work, such as a comfortable trot, can lead to overheating, dehydration and electrolyte imbalances if carried on for several hours.

When working an aged horse in hot weather, never exceed the limits of what he has been conditioned to do under similar weather conditions. His usual workout in the spring could be too stressful in hot and humid weather. Some sweating is unavoidable—and even desirable as this is how the horse cools himself—but he should not be worked to the point that a lather forms. Similarly, work always involves a rise in heart rate, respiratory rate and body temperature, but his pulse and breathing should return to levels not exceeding twice normal in three to five minutes and temperature to near normal (no greater than 100 degrees) in the same time period. You should be thoroughly familiar with your horse's normal resting pulse, respiratory rate, and temperature and use these to guide you in working him. Respiratory rates and temperatures are simple to obtain, although it is often difficult to feel the pulse, particularly if the horse is agitated and moving around. In these circumstances it may be easier to determine the heart rate by sliding your hand under his left elbow to feel the pulse.

Special care should be given to adequately warming up and cooling down the aged horse. A good general guideline is 10 minutes of strong walking before and after any work. The cool-down walking may be interrupted at the five-minute mark to evaluate the breathing, heart rate and temperature. When you have finished walking, remove all tack and sponge or hose the horse off with cool water. He may then be given access to hay and water as long as he is not consuming more than a half bucket or so (one to two gallons) of water at any one time. If his thirst seems greater than this, allow him to have no more than half a bucket and then offer the same amount at 15- to 20-minute intervals until he is satisfied. Horses who do not recover to acceptable pulse, respiration or temperature should be given only sips of water at five- to ten-minute intervals until they have returned to normal. Unrestricted access to water may result in colic and even founder as the blood normally supplying the intestines is busy working in the muscles until the horse is properly cooled.

No shortcuts should be taken in cooling out any horse, particularly an aged horse. It is known from other species that even very athletic individuals can suffer from sudden death if they work hard and stop suddenly. This can happen even when the cardiovascular system is perfectly normal. However, the changes in circulatory and cardiac efficiency accompanying aging make the tolerance to such sudden changes in activity even more dangerous.

Electrolyte Supplementation

Electrolytes are minerals that exist inside the horse's body in an electrically charged form. The cells of the body work like tiny batteries, maintaining a different concentration of electrolytes inside the cells than there is in the fluid surrounding the cells or in the bloodstream. The horse needs to take in enough electrolytes/minerals to keep the concentration of the key electrolytes both inside and outside the cells at a normal level. If he doesn't, the cells will not function properly.

When the horse is not being worked, his need for electrolytes is met by a properly balanced and supplemented diet and by having access to as much salt as he wants. Even in hot weather, there is no need for special electrolyte supplements if the horse is eating normally and taking in enough salt. In very hot and humid weather, the horse will need to consume three to four ounces of salt a day to match what he loses in his sweat. (He is sweating more when it's hot—even if the horse doesn't appear to you to be wet.) This would mean that the average stall-sized salt brick, which weighs four pounds, would last the horse about three weeks. If the horse cannot be confirmed to be taking in that much salt, or when formal exercise is added to the routine, an electrolyte supplement should be used.

Electrolyte Supplements

We already mentioned the horse will get everything he needs when not working if he eats a normal balanced and supplemented diet and takes in enough salt on his own. Electrolyte supplements are needed only when the sweat loss caused by exercise is added to those maintenance requirements.

It only makes sense to choose a supplement that matches the percentages and total amounts of electrolytes lost with sweating during exercise. Unfortunately, of the many, many electrolyte supplements on the market only a few actually do that. The list below notes the proportions of electrolytes lost in sweat. Choose a product that matches that profile.

ELECTROLYTE LOSSES IN SWEAT

	AMOUNT
SODIUM	20% to 25%
POTASSIUM	15% to 20%
CHLORIDE	45% to 55%
MAGNESIUM AND CALCIUM	about 1%

Choosing the right supplement would be easy if all product labels listed their ingredients this way. Many do not, so you will need to know how to translate. You will commonly find a label lists salt instead of sodium and chloride individually.

Salt is NaCl—sodium chloride. It is 40% sodium by weight and 60% chloride. Therefore if a product lists 80% salt, it will contain 32% sodium (40% of 80%) unless there are other chemicals in there that add to the sodium content (there usually are not). The total chloride in the product may come from the salt only or may be the sum of the chloride from the salt and the chloride from other minerals like potassium chloride. Potassium chloride (KCl) contains 47% potassium and 53% chloride.

Labels will usually list their ingredients as amounts per ounce, the common serving size. Choose one that provides 2.8 grams (or 2,800 mg) of sodium per ounce. This is about the amount you would need to feed if you worked the horse at a reasonable pace for an hour. The potassium per ounce should be a little bit less to match sweat but no less than 2,200 mg. Some products contain slightly more potassium. Up to about 3,200 mg of potassium per ounce is okay, too. Chloride needs to be about 4,700 mg/oz of product. Again, products vary in the exact amount they will contain but don't stray too far from this number. A range of about 4,500 mg to 5,000 mg (or 4.5 to 5.0 grams per ounce of product) would be fine. Calcium and magnesium losses are not as significant unless the horse is worked for several hours. However, one or both are usually included as well. Look for amounts of at least 150 to 200 mg of calcium and magnesium combined. A 2:1 ratio of calcium to magnesium is ideal.

Some electrolyte products contain additional minerals as well. These will not be needed if you are following the feeding and supplement recommendations in Chapters Three and Four. They also add to the price, so don't worry about buying a product that includes other minerals unless it is the only one you can find that has the correct percentages and total amounts of the important electrolytes.

Dextrose or other sugars (e.g., sucrose, glucose) are often added. This helps improve absorption of electrolytes but is not absolutely essential. The proteins glycine and betaine also help the body absorb and retain both electrolytes and water and are found in some products.

How to Give Electrolyte Supplements

Electrolytes can be added to water, added to feed or given as a paste. If added to the water supply, the horse should also be provided with a source of plain water since some horses will not drink, or will not drink enough, if you add electrolytes to their water.

If the horse will not voluntarily drink electrolytes in his water, try adding them to the feed—dividing the total daily dose between feedings. Most horses will consume their electrolytes this way.

If you still cannot get the electrolytes into the horse because he leaves them sitting in the feed trough or refuses to eat when they are in his feed, you will have to give them as a paste.

There are electrolyte pastes available, but I have not seen one yet that accurately matches sweat losses. They are also extremely expensive. A better approach is to mix your electrolyte supplement powder with a little water to form a paste and give this to the horse using a dose syringe. You can use an old, washed-out syringe from another product like a dewormer, but these are not made to be reusable and can be difficult to get apart, put back together and depress after that first use. Spraying a little cooking oil spray on the end of the plunger often makes them much easier to operate. You can also buy a 60 cc dose syringe from your veterinarian. These have a tapered, wide end that allows paste to go through much more easily than with a regular injection syringe.

Again, use some cooking oil spray to make them slide easier.

Skin Problems

The summer months are commonly associated with a variety of dif-
ficult-to-treat skin problems. Among the worst of these is onchocer-
ciasis. This is a condition characterized by hair loss, crusting, scaling,
swelling, redness and open oozing areas on the ventral midline
(belly) and sometimes on the face. It is caused in most cases by the
immature forms of a parasite, Onchocerca cervicalis, that in its
innocuous adult form is transmitted to horses via biting insects and
inhabits the large ligament on the top of the neck. This parasite produces tremendous numbers of immature forms, called microfilaria,
that then travel in the tissues under the skin and set up irritation in
the areas mentioned. Most cases are also complicated by irritation
from flies attracted to oozing areas of flesh and by secondary bacterial infection. A parasite called Draschia can also cause similar skin
problems.

These parasites can be very effectively treated by use of the
deworming drug ivermectin (see Chapter Seven). Regular use of
this drug can virtually eliminate problems with summer dermatitis.
Consult your vet first since it is often advisable to also treat the horse
with corticosteroids or antihistamines. Killing off large numbers of
these parasites may produce an allergic reaction in the horse.

These and other parasites may also be the cause of periodic ophthalmia, moonblindness. Use of ivermectin can cause a flare-up of
this disease or even a first time episode if they are present in the eye
as well. This is another reason to ask your vet about protecting the
horse with a short course of anti-inflammatory steroids or antihista-

mines before treating with ivermectin.

The secondary problems are controlled by cleansing the affected areas with plain or antibacterial soaps and removing all crusts. An antibacterial cream, sometimes containing steroids, is then applied, and fly repellent is used generously around the edges of the area. The area should be attended to at least twice daily (more frequent treatments are often necessary early in the treatment). If the horse is on turnout and/or if it is difficult to have someone treat him this often, move him to other quarters where he can be treated aggressively, at least for the first week or so. Similarly, if flies are a great problem, it may be necessary to arrange to have him stabled until the open areas of flesh are healed. Flies can be such a problem that some cases of midline dermatitis appear to be caused by flies alone. Investment in a long-lasting fly repellent, such as a gel from your veterinarian, is essential to the well-being of any animal kept on turnout in the summer months.

Another problem in the summer is habronemiasis—summer sores. This is a huge, granulating infection, often on the back of the pasterns, caused by infection of a break in the skin with the larvae of the stomach worm habronema. The eggs of this parasite are ingested by flies and mature to the larval stage within the fly. Open wounds become infected when larvae emerge from flies that are feeding on them. These parasites are also very effectively killed by ivermectin.

Scratches, or grease heel, is another skin problem in the pastern area that particularly plagues horses kept on turnout. It is an infection of the skin that follows small scratches from rough brasses, burrs or twigs. In severe cases, the entire leg to the knee can swell, and the small vessels that carry lymphatic fluid can become involved and scarred, leading to a permanently swollen leg. Horses with long hair at the fetlock and pastern are particularly prone to severe infections. Treatment involves clipping and cleansing the involved areas with an application of a drying wound powder to the area. Ointments and sprays should generally be avoided. It is best to prevent this problem from ever occurring by clipping the lower legs of hairy horses and inspecting horses regularly to detect and treat small skin breaks. Regular mowing and removal of burrs or other irritating plants from the horse's pasture are also advisable.

In summer, horses may also develop bacterial and fungal infections. This is usually a problem with horses on constant turnout which get repeatedly soaked with rain and are rarely groomed. Treatment is described under winter problems.

The summer months are also the time for sunburn in light-skinned horses such as Appaloosas or palominos and for a wide range of allergic reactions characterized by bumps or even open areas on the skin. The only way to avoid sunburn is to keep the horse out of the sun, although you may wish to try sunscreens or zinc oxide ointment (the white cream that lifeguards use) on sensitive areas when the horse is turned out or worked. Most allergic reactions are caused by insect bites, and again investment in a long-lasting gel insect repellent is essential.

The seasonal problems of older horses are much the same as for younger animals. With all management questions in caring for aged horses, consider their decreased resistance to disease and increased susceptibility to stress. Anything that interferes with the nutrition or water and electrolyte balance of the aged horse is likely to have far more serious consequences than with younger and more resilient animals. Finally, constant turnout and/or long periods of time without regular handling put the aged horse at higher risk for developing many seasonal health problems. Every effort must be made to prevent problems or to catch them in the early stages.

CHAPTER SIXTEEN

SAYING GOOD-BYE

If you have reached the point where your horse is being retired, chances are you should consider the issue of euthanasia.

No owner wishes to see his horse suffer. The decision to put a horse down is a difficult one, particularly if it is based on the quality of life rather than a clear-cut catastrophe.

On a practical level, there are certain measures you should take to guarantee your horse will never have to suffer because you could not be located to give permission for euthanasia. To begin with, the parties caring for the horse should have a current and workable set of phone numbers, preferably for more than one family member. If you are going to be away, even for only a day, be sure that you can be reached in case of an emergency.

It is advisable to designate someone to act on your behalf if you cannot be contacted. This should be a knowledgeable friend or trainer.

You may also opt to give your veterinarian a signed permission for anesthesia or euthanasia in case an emergency situation arises and allow him to do what he feels is best.

Discuss with your agent and/or veterinarian exactly what your wishes would be. For example, you might decide that surgery for a broken bone would not be worth the pain the horse would endure but if the problem was colic you would want the vet to try to save the horse. It is impossible to predict all eventualities and you may decide on no surgery under any circumstances or only if there is an excellent chance the horse will recover to live out his life comfortably.

In the last analysis your agent will have to exercise his own judgment, and all involved must be comfortable with this. Do not put vague constraints on this person such as, "If it's possible, try to wait until I get back. . . ." Your agent must be free to act in the horse's best interest.

When designating an agent, it is best to put the arrangement in writing. This can save critical time if the veterinarian or hospital attending to the horse in the emergency does not know you, since they must be very careful to avoid an unauthorized euthanasia. The document need not be elaborate. The following is a sample.

I, _____, authorize _____ to act in my absence regarding all emergency decisions on medical/surgical treatment or euthanasia for the horse _____(name)_____, tatoo _____, a _____-year old, ____(color)_____, _____(sex)_____.

Owner _____
Witness _____
Date _____

If you do go to the trouble of designating an agent, be sure to keep the document with the horse, e.g., in the barn office or your tack trunk, where it will be readily accessible.

If the horse is insured, the company will usually require notification prior to euthanasia or surgery. Attach the appropriate names and phone numbers of people to contact to your other emergency information and make sure everyone is aware of the situation in advance. Also, if you do make arrangements for an agent, inform the insurance company of these details. An emergency is no time for lengthy explanations to the insurance company.

As a final practical consideration, give some thought to disposal of the body. Burying a horse is a major undertaking, and there may also be local regulations prohibiting this practice or dictating depth of burial. It is advisable to not only have a site reserved, but to plan in detail how the horse will be moved and what will be used to dig the hole.

Most people opt to have the body removed and disposed of by a renderer. These can be found in the yellow pages in most localities, and there is no need to make prearrangements. Renderers are usually very good about arriving promptly. Most will also euthanize the horse for you (bullet to the brain) if you so wish and actually do a very neat and professional job. However, there is nothing dignified in the sight of a horse being hoisted into a truck by chains, so you may want to arrange not to be present for this. It is not necessary to be on the premises when the renderer arrives, but someone should be present to give the authorization to euthanize the horse and remove the body. You should identify this party to the renderer when you make the arrangements.

The moment will be over for the horse before he realizes anything is going on, so the decision of whether to remain for the proceedings is up to the individual owner. Most would prefer to say their last good-byes and then leave.

Accepting euthanasia in theory, and even providing for the eventuality, is miles away from reality. Many, if not most, horses will not die of natural causes.

When the question arises suddenly, as with a severe colic or broken bone, owners often feel pressured, confused and overwhelmed. These very understandable emotions may be intensified if the veterinarian involved is a stranger.

It is vitally important for the horse's sake that you remember the veterinarian has the horse's best interests in mind. No one enjoys destroying an animal or makes the recommendation lightly. Try to remain calm, listen carefully to the reasons euthanasia is being suggested and ask questions until you understand. You could also ask for a second opinion if this request would not cause an inordinate delay. If you are having trouble reaching a decision, be guided by how much the horse is suffering and/or is likely to suffer.

I recall a quarter horse that was brought into New Bolton Center in the early stages of botulism poisoning. This disease causes a progressive paralysis with inability to move or stand, inability to swallow and eventual paralysis of the respiratory muscles. Most horses panic and become unmanageable fairly early in the course of the disease.

This horse, however, was almost unbelievably intelligent, trusting and cooperative. He conserved his energy and therefore was better able to help us when we periodically got him to his feet in a sling. He even had the sense to alternate the side he would go down on when he tired. The owners were several hours away from the hospital but were in regular phone contact and had been informed of the very poor prognosis in attempts to prepare them for the worst.

The horse held his own for 48 hours but then began to show the telltale changes in his breathing that signaled the paralysis was worsening and his lungs filling with fluid. Even in the short time he had been in the hospital, everyone developed a strong bond of respect and admiration for this horse. He knew he was fighting for his life and also knew he was losing the battle.

The owners were contacted and asked to give permission for euthanasia. They were told that the disease progresses rapidly once the point of altered breathing is reached and that the horse would eventually suffocate. They were told the horse was dying, but despite this felt they could not possibly give permission until they saw him for themselves.

The following hours were pure hell for the horse and those caring for him. By the time his owners arrived, his once clear, expressive eyes were filled with panic, his mouth was blue, and he was covered with sweat and straw from struggling against his invisible attacker. Permission for euthanasia was given then, but instead of providing a peaceful, dignified release it was a struggle to wrestle him still long enough to infuse the drug that would finalize his defeat.

Every equine veterinarian has been faced with some variation of this dilemma where the owner is not present and hesitates to give permission for euthanasia. It is easy to become too involved in your own feelings of loss at the expense of the horse. The kindest and most difficult thing is to have the courage to say good-bye.

As horrible as these agonal scenes are, equally tragic are the horses condemned to a life with constant pain or disability. Natural deaths virtually never are a tranquil going to sleep on a full stomach, never to awaken. If the horse does not succumb to an acute catastrophe, such as colic or injury, he may linger for many months unable to obtain sufficient food, water or shelter until malnutrition, dehydration and weakness claim him.

No one wants to be guilty of such neglect, but the fact is that it is often very difficult to clearly see how much a horse has deteriorated when the downhill course is a slow one. It is also very difficult to reach a decision for euthanasia if your old friend is still functional at any level.

300

There are some reasonable steps you can take to avoid letting matters get out of hand. To begin, when you decide to retire the horse, make a list of all his problems such as lameness, respiratory disease, visual defects and so forth. Next, ask your veterinarian to describe how the disease progresses, what to look for at each stage and how the advancing disease will affect the horse's daily life. For example, when a horse is on turnout, there are several telltale signs that he is losing the ability to function. Such horses are often isolated from others as they seek to avoid any chance of a confrontation from which they cannot defend themselves or flee. These horses are also the last to get feed or water, if they get it at all, and will hang back when the group is rounded up. They may also spend increasing amounts of time lying down. Eventually, coat quality and weight begin to drop off, sure signs the horse has been significantly stressed for quite some time.

Finally, decide in advance what your course of action will be. You may elect to euthanize a horse with eye problems when he first starts to bump into things, instead of waiting for a serious injury. With a lameness problem, you may draw the line when he has trouble competing for food, or with a heavy horse when even a walk to the water causes flaring of his nostrils and uncontrollable coughing. If you have trouble realistically evaluating the horse, ask the opinion of your veterinarian or any other knowledgeable person who does not see the horse as regularly as you do. Their perspective can be very helpful and they may give you an entirely different opinion on how well the horse is doing.

The use of functional guidelines may seem arbitrary, even trivial. However, all are symptomatic of a horse with severe problems adapting to the routine activities of daily living and correspond to an underlying physical compromise. If you understand the disease process and attempt to humanely and intelligently decide where to draw the line, you will take a major step toward assuring your horse's last days are truly enjoyable and peaceful.

INDEX

A

Abdominal tumors (lipomas), 188
Abortion, 252
Abscesses and colic, 198
Absorbine, 144
ACTH, 169
Acupuncture
    for arthritis, 148
    for navicular disease, 171
Adrenal
    glands and metabolism, 17
    tumors, 176
Agent, designating, 296, 297
Aging, 1–9
    antibiotics and, 3
    biological clock and, 4–6, 5
    car engine analogy, 6, 9
    DNA and, 4–6, 5
    infections, control of, 3, 195–96
    life span, 1, 3–4
    medical profession's view of, vii–viii

premature aging, 2, 6, 9, 53–54
preventable causes of, 6, 9
RNA and, 5–6
telomeres, 5–6
vaccines, 3
See also Alternative and complementary
    medicine; Arthritis; Broodmare
    management; Diet and nutrition;
    Environmental toxins; Euthanasia;
    Exercise; Health care, routine; Health
    problems; Hormonal function;
    Older horse management; Preventable
    causes of aging; Purchasing older horses;
    Stallion management; Summer care;
    Supplements; Winter care
Alcohol blocks for lameness, 259
Alfalfa
    for broodmares, 261
    cubes for winter, 277
    meal protein, 59
    minerals in, 51, 70–71
    pellet (Piperazine), 127–28

protein, 39
Black, Lynn, 13
Blankets for winter, 274, 275, 282
Blister beetles, 48–49
Blood sugar and diet, 34
Blood tests, veterinary exam, 239–40
Bloodworms (large strongyles), 123, 128
Body Builder, 179, 180, 261
Body disposal, 297–98
Bony look of horse, 92, 94
Bots, 124, 125, 126, 128
Botulism, 117–18
Brans, 34, 35, 36
Breeding history, broodmare, 265–67
Brewer's Yeast, 55, 57
Bright Zip, 7
Bromelain, 56
Bromocriptine, 177
Bronchodilators for respiratory problems, 192
Broodmare management, 249–68
    abortion, 252
    alcohol blocks for lameness, 259
    analgesic drugs, effect on fetus, 258
    antibiotics for uterine infections, 253–54
    auctions, 265–68
    barren mares, 266
    Caslick's operation, 255
    chromosomal defects, 256
    conformation and reproductive-tract infections, 255
    diet and nutrition, 259–65
    digestive tract, decreased efficiency, 259–60
    estrogen for uterine infections, 254
    foaling and uterine infections, 254–55
    hematocrit testing, 262–63
    hemoglobin testing, 262–63
    hemorrhage of uterine artery, 257–58
    history, breeding, 265–67
    housing for, 250, 251
    lactation, 261–62
    lameness and pregnancy, 258–59
    metabolic bone disease, 263–64
    minerals for, 260–61, 262–64
    nerve blocks for lameness, 259
    neurectomy for lameness, 259
    open mares, 266
    osteochondrosis dessicans, 263
    osteoporosis, 263

    Owner's Statement, 266
    physical changes, 250, 251
    Pitocin for uterine infections, 254
    pregnancy loss, 256
    progesterone levels, 256
    purchasing at auctions, 265–68
    rising plane of nutrition, 260
    sensitivity testing, 253
    steroid drugs, effect on fetus, 258
    supplements for, 261
    surgery for conformation problems, 255–56
    trace minerals for, 260, 261, 264
    urine pooling, 255
    uterine artery hemorrhage, 257–58
    uterine infections, 251–56
    vagina, tipping in, 251, 255
    vitamins for, 260–61, 262
    weight gain, 261
    See also Diet and nutrition, brood mares; Older horse management
Buckeye Nutrition, 280
Bulk (nondigestible fiber), 33–34
Bursitis, 160–61
Bute. See Phenylbutazone
B vitamins
    for broodmares, 261, 262
    for immune system, 195
    for older horses, 212
    supplements, 65–66, 72–73

C

Calcium
    for broodmares, 262, 263
    in diet, 35, 46, 47, 51
    in summer, 288, 289
    supplements, 60, 71
Calorie restriction and aging, 12–13, 13, 15–16
Calories (energy), 26, 33
Canadian Veterinary Journal, 78
Cancer, 185–89
Capsicum rubs for arthritis, 157
Captan, 283
Carbohydrates, 44–46
Carcinomas, 187
Cardiovascular system of stallions, 269
Car engine analogy of aging, 6, 9
Carson, Rachel, 78
Cartilage, exercise for, 96–97

Gray horses and melanomas, 186
Grease heel (scratches), 292–93
Grooming in winter, 282
Growth hormone, 178, 180
Gut scratch factor, 33–34

H

Habits, bad, 217–18
Habronemiasis (summer sores), 292
Half round shoes, 109–10
Hays
for broodmares, 260–61
chopped hay, 206
fiber in, 36
minerals in, 51, 70–71
for older horses, 205, 206
protein in, 38, 59
vitamins in, 64, 67, 72–73
for winter, 277, 278–79
See also Alfalfa; Grass
Health care, routine, 107–28
barefoot, benefits of, 108–9, 136
bioflavinoids for immune system, 115
botulism, 117–18
coffin bone, 111
deep flexor tendon, 111
dental care, 112–14
digestion and teeth, 112–13
digital cushion, 111
Eastern encephalitis, 118
encephalitis, 116
foot (hoof) care, 107–12, 111
four point trim, 110–12
half round shoes, 109–10
heels of foot, 111, 112
influenza, 114–15, 276
natural foot, 110–11
for older horses, 211, 212–14
pastern, 111
Potomac Horse Fever (PHF), 118
quarters of hoof, 111, 112
rabies, 116–17
rhinopneumonitis (rhino), 114–15, 276
shoes, 109–10
strangles, 115-16
teeth floating, 31, 31–32, 113
tetanus, 115-16
toe of hoof, 111–12
trimming cautions, 110–12, 161
vaccinations, 3, 114–19, 214, 275–76

Venezuelan encephalitis, 118
vitamin C for immune system, 115
Western encephalitis, 118
West Nile encephalitis, 118–19
See also Deworming; Health problems
Health problems, 185–201
abdominal tumors (lipomas), 188
abscesses and colic, 198
allergies, 191–92
antibiotics for moonblindness, 200
antibiotics for respiratory problems, 192
antihistamines for respiratory problems, 192
antioxidants for immune system, 195
Appaloosas and moonblindness, 199–200
arabanogalactin for immune system, 196
arrhythmias, 189–90
arteries, ruptured, 189
beet feed for, 193
bioflavinoids for moonblindness, 200
bronchodilators for respiratory problems, 192
B vitamins for immune system, 195
cancer, 185–89
carcinomas, 187
chemotherapy for tumors, 188
choke, 196–97
chronic obstructive pulmonary disease (COPD), 191–92, 192
Cimetidine for tumors, 186
coenzyme Q10 (CoQ10) for respiratory problems, 193–94
colic, 197–98
corticosteroids for moonblindness, 200
corticosteroids for respiratory problems, 192
dental care and intestinal problems, 197, 198
diet and, 195–96, 197, 198
from environmental toxins, 188, 190
equine recurrent uveitis (ERU), 199–201, 291–92
exercise and heart problems, 189–90
feed and respiratory problems, 193
grape-seed extract for moonblindness, 200
grape-seed extract for respiratory problems, 194
gray horses and melanomas, 186

Worming. See Deworming

X

X-rays, veterinary exam, 235, 238–39

Y

YeaSacc, 57
Yeast, 55, 57
Yucca for arthritis, 156–57

Z

Zimecterin (ivermectin), 126
Zinc
    as antioxidant enzyme, 19
    for broodmares, 260, 261, 263–64
    supplements, 62, 71